Math 3

An Incremental Development

Student Workbook (Part Two)

Nancy Larson

with

Jeanne Honore Miller
Sharon Molster Orio

Saxon Publishers, Inc.

Math 3: An Incremental Development

Student Workbook

Copyright © 1997 by Saxon Publishers, Inc. and Nancy Larson

Printed in the United States of America

ISBN 13: 978-0-939798-83-4 (set)
ISBN 13: 978-1-56577-452-0 (wb.1)
ISBN 13: 978-1-56577-453-7 (wb. 2)

Editor: Deborah Williams
Production Supervisor: David Pond
Graphic Artists: Scott Kirby, John Chitwood, Gary Skidmore,
                  Tim Maltz, and Chad Threet

14 15 16 0928 14 13 12
4500364281

Reaching us via the Internet

www.saxonpublishers.com

E-mail: info@saxonpublishers.com

3 × 5	5 × 5	1 × 5	7 × 5	5 × 4
5 × 6	0 × 5	9 × 5	5 × 2	5 × 8
0 × 5	5 × 9	4 × 5	5 × 2	7 × 5
5 × 6	5 × 1	5 × 5	8 × 5	3 × 5
2 × 5	5 × 7	5 × 3	5 × 8	6 × 5

Score: _____

3-73Fa

6	10	4	9	10
− 2	− 3	− 1	− 4	− 5

10	8	15	10	7
− 8	− 4	− 7	− 7	− 2

11	10	5	12	10
− 5	− 7	− 2	− 6	− 2

10	7	10	3	13
− 4	− 1	− 9	− 2	− 6

10	10	16	10	8
− 6	− 0	− 8	− 10	− 2

Score: _____

3-73Fb

Name _____ •

Date _____ •

(Draw a 10 cm line segment. Measure it using inches. _____ ")

(Draw a $3\frac{1}{2}$" line segment. Measure it using centimeters. _____ cm)

1. Emily needs new tape on the edge of her bedroom rug. The rug is 6 feet long and 4 feet wide. Draw a small picture of the rug. How much tape will she need to buy?

   Number sentence _____

   Answer _____

2. There are ten children in the hot lunch line. You are the fourth person in line.

   How many children are in front of you? _____

   How many children are behind you? _____

3. Write these numbers using words.

   63 _____

   48 _____

4. Write the first ten perfect squares.

   _____ _____ _____ _____ _____ _____ _____ _____ _____ _____

5. How many large squares are there? _____

   How much is shaded? _____

   Circle the amount that is not shaded. $1\frac{1}{4}$, $1\frac{2}{4}$, $1\frac{3}{4}$,   1, $\frac{1}{4}$

6. Write these numbers using digits.

   two hundred fifty _____   four hundred nine _____

7. Use the correct comparison symbol (>, <, or =).

   49 + 26 ☐ 52 + 25   5 × 6 ☐ 4 × 7

Name _____

Date _____

1. Denise also needs new tape on the edges of her bedroom rug. The rug is 7 feet long and 3 feet wide. Draw a small picture of the rug. How much tape will she need to buy?

   Number sentence _____

   Answer _____

2. There are eight people waiting to see the doctor. The nurse said you are fifth.

   How many people are before you? _____

   How many people are after you? _____

3. Write these numbers using words.

   85 _____

   62 _____

4. Circle the numbers that are perfect squares.

   9   20   16   50   49   24   100   1   18   4

5. How many circles are there? _____

   How much is shaded? _____

   Circle the amount that is not shaded. $2\frac{1}{2}$, $1\frac{1}{2}$, $\frac{1}{2}$,   1, $3\frac{1}{2}$

6. Write these numbers using digits.

   one hundred seven _____   four hundred sixty-three _____

7. Use the correct comparison symbol (>, <, or =).

   38 + 44 ☐ 57 + 22   4 × 5 ☐ 3 × 7

Name _____

3 × 5	5 × 5	1 × 5	7 × 5	5 × 4
5 × 6	0 × 5	9 × 5	5 × 2	5 × 8
0 × 5	5 × 9	4 × 5	5 × 2	7 × 5
5 × 6	5 × 1	5 × 5	8 × 5	3 × 5
2 × 5	5 × 7	5 × 3	5 × 8	6 × 5

Score: _____

3-74Fa

$$
\begin{array}{r} 3 \\ \times\ 3 \\ \hline \end{array}
\qquad
\begin{array}{r} 9 \\ \times\ 9 \\ \hline \end{array}
\qquad
\begin{array}{r} 5 \\ \times\ 5 \\ \hline \end{array}
\qquad
\begin{array}{r} 7 \\ \times\ 7 \\ \hline \end{array}
\qquad
\begin{array}{r} 2 \\ \times\ 2 \\ \hline \end{array}
$$

$$
\begin{array}{r} 6 \\ \times\ 6 \\ \hline \end{array}
\qquad
\begin{array}{r} 1 \\ \times\ 1 \\ \hline \end{array}
\qquad
\begin{array}{r} 8 \\ \times\ 8 \\ \hline \end{array}
\qquad
\begin{array}{r} 4 \\ \times\ 4 \\ \hline \end{array}
\qquad
\begin{array}{r} 10 \\ \times\ 10 \\ \hline \end{array}
$$

$$
\begin{array}{r} 0 \\ \times\ 0 \\ \hline \end{array}
\qquad
\begin{array}{r} 5 \\ \times\ 5 \\ \hline \end{array}
\qquad
\begin{array}{r} 9 \\ \times\ 9 \\ \hline \end{array}
\qquad
\begin{array}{r} 7 \\ \times\ 7 \\ \hline \end{array}
\qquad
\begin{array}{r} 2 \\ \times\ 2 \\ \hline \end{array}
$$

$$
\begin{array}{r} 4 \\ \times\ 4 \\ \hline \end{array}
\qquad
\begin{array}{r} 8 \\ \times\ 8 \\ \hline \end{array}
\qquad
\begin{array}{r} 1 \\ \times\ 1 \\ \hline \end{array}
\qquad
\begin{array}{r} 6 \\ \times\ 6 \\ \hline \end{array}
\qquad
\begin{array}{r} 3 \\ \times\ 3 \\ \hline \end{array}
$$

$$
\begin{array}{r} 5 \\ \times\ 5 \\ \hline \end{array}
\qquad
\begin{array}{r} 7 \\ \times\ 7 \\ \hline \end{array}
\qquad
\begin{array}{r} 10 \\ \times\ 10 \\ \hline \end{array}
\qquad
\begin{array}{r} 0 \\ \times\ 0 \\ \hline \end{array}
\qquad
\begin{array}{r} 8 \\ \times\ 8 \\ \hline \end{array}
$$

Score: _____

Name •

(Draw a 95 mm line segment.)

Date •

(Draw a 6 cm 2 mm line segment.)

1. Ann had some money. Her mother gave her 60¢. Now she has 85¢. How much money did Ann have before?

   Number sentence _____

   Answer _____

2. There are seven people in line. You are the fifth person in line.

   How many people are before you? _____

   How many people are after you? _____

3. Write 38 using words. _____

   Write three hundred fifty using digits. _____

4. Circle the unit of measure you would use to measure the height of a dog.

   miles   pounds   quarts   inches   yards

5. What are the smudged digits?

   $4 + \mathbf{\xi} + 7 = 7 + 4 + 9$ ____

   $5 + 5 + 5 + 5 + 5 + 5 = \mathbf{\xi} \times 5$ ____

6. Label each fractional part of the hexagon.

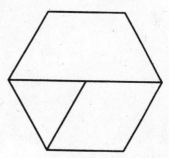

7. Fill in the missing numbers.

   $36 = $ _____ tens and 16 ones $45 = 3$ tens and _____ ones

   $58 = $ _____ tens and 8 ones $72 = 7$ tens and _____ ones

Name _____   **LESSON 74B**

Date _____   *Math 3*

1. Peter had some baseball cards. His aunt gave him 25 more cards. Now he has 65 baseball cards. How many baseball cards did Peter have before?

    Number sentence _____

    Answer _____

2. There are ten people in line. You are the seventh person in line.

    How many people are before you? _____

    How many people are after you? _____

3. Write 53 using words. _____

    Write two hundred seventy using digits. _____

4. Circle the unit of measure you might use to measure the amount of flour for a recipe.

    cups   inches   yards   tons   centimeters

5. What are the smudged digits?

    $3 + 6 + ⬤ = 6 + 8 + 3$ $7 + 7 + 7 + 7 + 7 = ⬤ \times 7$

    ____   ____

6. Label each fractional part of the hexagon.

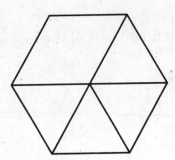

7. Fill in the missing numbers.

    $28 = $ _____ tens and 8 ones $52 = 5$ tens and _____ ones

    $39 = $ _____ tens and 19 ones $73 = 6$ tens and _____ ones

3-74Wb

1. Ben reads 4 pages each evening. How many pages will he read in 1 week?

   Number sentence _____ Answer _____

2. Jenny had 20 markers. Her sister gave her some more markers. Now Jenny has 84 markers. How many markers did Jenny's sister give her?

   Number sentence _____

   Answer _____

3. How many letters are there in the word Alaska? _____   ALASKA

   How many letters are vowels? _____

   What fractional part is this? _____

   How many letters are consonants? _____

   What fractional part is this? _____

4. I have 5 ten-dollar bills, 6 one-dollar bills, and 2 hundred-dollar bills.

   How much money do I have? _____

5. Shade the cups to show the following amounts.

   $\frac{1}{2}$ cup $\frac{1}{4}$ cup $\frac{2}{3}$ cup $\frac{3}{4}$ cup

6. Measure each line segment.

   segment DE = _____ cm

   segment EF = _____ cm

   segment DF = _____ cm

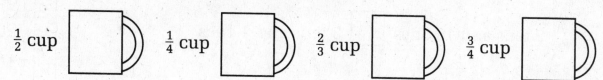

7. I have 2 quarters, 2 dimes, 3 nickels, and 6 pennies. Draw the coins.

How much money is this? _____

8. Find the answers.

620 − 200 = _____   16 × 10 = _____   430 + 300 = _____

87 − 50 = _____   58 + 31 = _____   25 × 10 = _____

2 × 6 = _____   7 × 8 = _____   90 ÷ 10 = _____

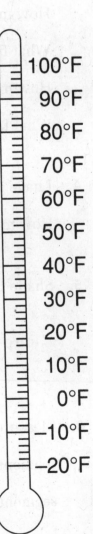

9. Shade the thermometer to show 37°F.

At what temperature does water freeze? _____

10. Use the correct comparison symbol (>, <, or =).

22 ⬜ 7 + 8 + 3 + 4   2 × 10 ⬜ 3 × 7

2 tens and 16 ones ⬜ 3 tens and 4 ones

420 + 200 ⬜ 63 × 10

Name _____

Today's Date is _____

Today's Pattern _____

_____

Coin Cup

Q	D	N	P	Total Coins

Today's Problem

Today's Date is _____

Today's Pattern _____

_____

Coin Cup

Q	D	N	P	Total Coins

Today's Problem

Today's Date is _____

Today's Pattern _____

_____

Coin Cup

Q	D	N	P	Total Coins

Today's Problem

Today's Date is _____

Today's Pattern _____

_____

Coin Cup

Q	D	N	P	Total Coins

Today's Problem

Today's Date is _____

Today's Pattern _____

_____

Coin Cup

Q	D	N	P	Total Coins

Today's Problem

$$\begin{array}{r} 4 \\ \times\ 4 \\ \hline \end{array} \qquad \begin{array}{r} 4 \\ \times\ 10 \\ \hline \end{array} \qquad \begin{array}{r} 1 \\ \times\ 4 \\ \hline \end{array} \qquad \begin{array}{r} 8 \\ \times\ 4 \\ \hline \end{array} \qquad \begin{array}{r} 4 \\ \times\ 3 \\ \hline \end{array}$$

$$\begin{array}{r} 4 \\ \times\ 5 \\ \hline \end{array} \qquad \begin{array}{r} 4 \\ \times\ 9 \\ \hline \end{array} \qquad \begin{array}{r} 6 \\ \times\ 4 \\ \hline \end{array} \qquad \begin{array}{r} 2 \\ \times\ 4 \\ \hline \end{array} \qquad \begin{array}{r} 4 \\ \times\ 7 \\ \hline \end{array}$$

$$\begin{array}{r} 0 \\ \times\ 4 \\ \hline \end{array} \qquad \begin{array}{r} 6 \\ \times\ 4 \\ \hline \end{array} \qquad \begin{array}{r} 4 \\ \times\ 4 \\ \hline \end{array} \qquad \begin{array}{r} 2 \\ \times\ 4 \\ \hline \end{array} \qquad \begin{array}{r} 4 \\ \times\ 9 \\ \hline \end{array}$$

$$\begin{array}{r} 4 \\ \times\ 7 \\ \hline \end{array} \qquad \begin{array}{r} 4 \\ \times\ 5 \\ \hline \end{array} \qquad \begin{array}{r} 4 \\ \times\ 1 \\ \hline \end{array} \qquad \begin{array}{r} 8 \\ \times\ 4 \\ \hline \end{array} \qquad \begin{array}{r} 3 \\ \times\ 4 \\ \hline \end{array}$$

$$\begin{array}{r} 4 \\ \times\ 10 \\ \hline \end{array} \qquad \begin{array}{r} 3 \\ \times\ 4 \\ \hline \end{array} \qquad \begin{array}{r} 4 \\ \times\ 5 \\ \hline \end{array} \qquad \begin{array}{r} 7 \\ \times\ 4 \\ \hline \end{array} \qquad \begin{array}{r} 4 \\ \times\ 0 \\ \hline \end{array}$$

Score: _____

Name ⬤
●
(Draw an 85 mm line segment.)

Date ●

(Draw an 8 cm 5 mm line segment.)

1. Connie needs 53¢ to buy a marker. She has 40¢. How much more money does she need?

   Number sentence _____

   Answer _____

2. Use these digit cards to make the number closest to 500. Use each digit card only once.

   2 4 7 ____

3. Write 94 using words. _____

   Write eight hundred twenty-seven using digits. _____

⬤ 4. Shade the cups to show each amount. $\frac{1}{3}$ cup $\frac{3}{4}$ cup

   How much more will you need to make one cup? ____   ____

5. Circle the combinations of coins that equal 68¢.

   2 quarters, 2 dimes, 3 pennies   1 quarter, 4 dimes, 3 pennies

   5 dimes, 18 pennies   2 quarters, 3 nickels, 8 pennies

6. Find each product.

   $\begin{array}{c}4\\ \times 5\end{array}$ $\begin{array}{c}4\\ \times 3\end{array}$ $\begin{array}{c}4\\ \times 8\end{array}$ $\begin{array}{c}4\\ \times 6\end{array}$ $\begin{array}{c}2\\ \times 4\end{array}$ $\begin{array}{c}9\\ \times 4\end{array}$ $\begin{array}{c}7\\ \times 4\end{array}$ $17 \times 10 =$ ____

   $42 \times 10 =$ ____

7. Find each sum.

⬤ $48 + 27 =$ ____ $24 + 56 =$ ____

   $4 + 8 + 2 + 3 + 7 + 8 + 9 + 1 + 6 + 5 =$ ____

Name _____ **LESSON 75B**
                                                    Math 3
Date _____

1. Debbie needs 72¢ to buy a notebook. She has 30¢. How much more money does she need?

   Number sentence _____

   Answer _____

2. Use these digit cards to make the number closest to 800. Use each digit card only once.

        ____

3. Write 72 using words. _____

   Write nine hundred eleven using digits. _____

4. Shade the cups to show each amount. $\frac{1}{4}$ cup 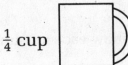 $\frac{2}{3}$ cup

   How much more will you need to make one cup?   ____   ____

5. Circle the combinations of coins that equal 82¢.

   3 quarters, 7 pennies   1 quarter, 5 dimes, 1 nickel, 2 pennies

   7 dimes, 12 pennies   2 quarters, 3 nickels, 2 pennies

6. Find each product.

   $\begin{array}{r} 4 \\ \times 7 \\ \hline \end{array}$ $\begin{array}{r} 2 \\ \times 4 \\ \hline \end{array}$ $\begin{array}{r} 4 \\ \times 8 \\ \hline \end{array}$ $\begin{array}{r} 5 \\ \times 4 \\ \hline \end{array}$ $\begin{array}{r} 9 \\ \times 4 \\ \hline \end{array}$ $\begin{array}{r} 4 \\ \times 4 \\ \hline \end{array}$ $\begin{array}{r} 4 \\ \times 6 \\ \hline \end{array}$ $23 \times 10 =$ _____

   $58 \times 10 =$ _____

7. Find each sum.

   $49 + 24 =$ _____ $17 + 43 =$ _____

   $2 + 4 + 3 + 7 + 9 + 8 + 6 + 5 + 1 + 2 + 3 =$ _____

Name _____

KEY

TITLE _____

Name _____

KEY

TITLE

Name _____

$$\begin{array}{r} 4 \\ \times\ 4 \\ \hline \end{array} \qquad \begin{array}{r} 4 \\ \times\ 10 \\ \hline \end{array} \qquad \begin{array}{r} 1 \\ \times\ 4 \\ \hline \end{array} \qquad \begin{array}{r} 8 \\ \times\ 4 \\ \hline \end{array} \qquad \begin{array}{r} 4 \\ \times\ 3 \\ \hline \end{array}$$

$$\begin{array}{r} 4 \\ \times\ 5 \\ \hline \end{array} \qquad \begin{array}{r} 4 \\ \times\ 9 \\ \hline \end{array} \qquad \begin{array}{r} 6 \\ \times\ 4 \\ \hline \end{array} \qquad \begin{array}{r} 2 \\ \times\ 4 \\ \hline \end{array} \qquad \begin{array}{r} 4 \\ \times\ 7 \\ \hline \end{array}$$

$$\begin{array}{r} 0 \\ \times\ 4 \\ \hline \end{array} \qquad \begin{array}{r} 6 \\ \times\ 4 \\ \hline \end{array} \qquad \begin{array}{r} 4 \\ \times\ 4 \\ \hline \end{array} \qquad \begin{array}{r} 2 \\ \times\ 4 \\ \hline \end{array} \qquad \begin{array}{r} 4 \\ \times\ 9 \\ \hline \end{array}$$

$$\begin{array}{r} 4 \\ \times\ 7 \\ \hline \end{array} \qquad \begin{array}{r} 4 \\ \times\ 5 \\ \hline \end{array} \qquad \begin{array}{r} 4 \\ \times\ 1 \\ \hline \end{array} \qquad \begin{array}{r} 8 \\ \times\ 4 \\ \hline \end{array} \qquad \begin{array}{r} 3 \\ \times\ 4 \\ \hline \end{array}$$

$$\begin{array}{r} 4 \\ \times\ 10 \\ \hline \end{array} \qquad \begin{array}{r} 3 \\ \times\ 4 \\ \hline \end{array} \qquad \begin{array}{r} 4 \\ \times\ 5 \\ \hline \end{array} \qquad \begin{array}{r} 7 \\ \times\ 4 \\ \hline \end{array} \qquad \begin{array}{r} 4 \\ \times\ 0 \\ \hline \end{array}$$

Score: _____

3-76Fa

Name <u>   </u>
    (Draw a 7 cm line segment.)

Date <u>   </u>

    (Draw a congruent line segment. It is ____ mm long.)

1. The movie begins at 6:45 p.m. It is a two-hour movie.

   At what time will the movie end? _____

2. Draw a line graph for the following temperatures.

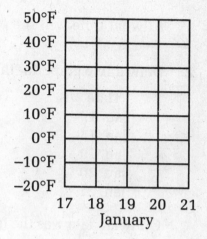

Date	Temperature
Jan. 17	5°F
Jan. 18	20°F
Jan. 19	−10°F
Jan. 20	37°F
Jan. 21	12°F

   On what date was the temperature the lowest? _____

3. Use these digit cards to make the following numbers. Use each digit card only once for each number.

    6 9 3

   largest 3-digit number _____   smallest 3-digit number _____

4. Measure the line segments using millimeters.

   What is the length of the oblique line segment? _____

   What is the length of the vertical line segment? _____

   What is the length of the horizontal line segment? _____

   What is the perimeter of the triangle? _____

5. Fill in the missing factors.

$$\frac{\begin{array}{r}\square \\ \times\ 4\end{array}}{32} \quad \frac{\begin{array}{r}4 \\ \times\ \square\end{array}}{20} \quad \frac{\begin{array}{r}\square \\ \times\ 4\end{array}}{36} \quad \frac{\begin{array}{r}\square \\ \times\ 4\end{array}}{12} \quad \frac{\begin{array}{r}\square \\ \times\ 2\end{array}}{14} \quad \frac{\begin{array}{r}7 \\ \times\ \square\end{array}}{42} \quad \frac{\begin{array}{r}\square \\ \times\ 10\end{array}}{60} \quad \frac{\begin{array}{r}5 \\ \times\ \square\end{array}}{40}$$

6. Complete the patterns. Find the rules.

   ____, ____, ____, 150, 175, 200, ____, ____, ____   Rule: _____

   ____, ____, ____, ____, ____, ____, 372, 362, 352   Rule: _____

Name _____

Date _____

Math 3

1. The play begins at 3:20 p.m. It is a one-hour play.

   At what time will the play end? _____

2. Draw a line graph for the following temperatures.

Date	Temperature
Jan. 17	40°F
Jan. 18	15°F
Jan. 19	−20°F
Jan. 20	18°F
Jan. 21	6°F

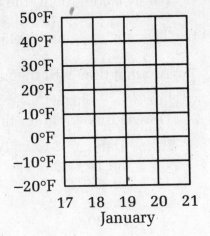

   On what date was the temperature the lowest? _____

3. Use these digit cards to make the following numbers. Use each digit card only once for each number.

     4 **8** **1**

   largest 3-digit number _____   number closest to 800 _____

4. Write the lengths of the line segments using centimeters.

   What is the length of the oblique line segment? _____

   What is the length of the vertical line segment? _____

   What is the length of the horizontal line segment? _____

   What is the perimeter of the triangle in centimeters? _____

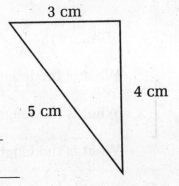

3 cm
4 cm
5 cm

5. Fill in the missing factors.

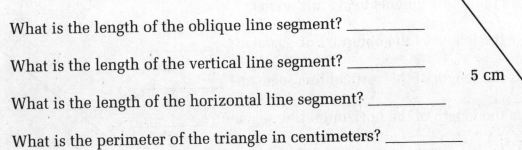

6. Complete the patterns. Find the rules.

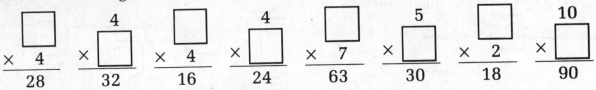

   _____, _____, _____, 525, 500, 475, _____, _____, _____   Rule: _____

   446, 436, 426, _____, _____, _____, _____, _____, _____   Rule: _____

3-76Wb

Copyright by Saxon Publishers, Inc. and Nancy Larson. Reproduction prohibited.

Date _____

PAY TO THE
ORDER OF _____ $ [   ]

_____ DOLLARS

_____

Date _____

PAY TO THE
ORDER OF _____ $ [   ]

_____ DOLLARS

_____

Date _____

PAY TO THE
ORDER OF _____ $ [   ]

_____ DOLLARS

_____

Name _____   Score: _____   **A2-100**

5 + 4	4 + 6	2 + 3	6 + 8	5 + 0	0 + 9	4 + 8	5 + 6	1 + 3	6 + 1
2 + 5	0 + 8	6 + 7	0 + 3	2 + 9	8 + 8	6 + 0	1 + 9	6 + 9	8 + 4
1 + 6	9 + 8	1 + 5	4 + 9	8 + 6	2 + 4	7 + 9	8 + 3	4 + 3	0 + 4
7 + 3	3 + 2	7 + 0	7 + 2	1 + 4	6 + 5	3 + 6	3 + 0	8 + 0	9 + 7
9 + 9	7 + 8	7 + 4	9 + 5	5 + 7	1 + 8	0 + 1	8 + 9	2 + 7	7 + 5
0 + 7	6 + 6	3 + 3	2 + 6	6 + 2	9 + 2	5 + 8	4 + 5	9 + 3	3 + 1
5 + 1	4 + 1	8 + 1	3 + 4	0 + 0	4 + 4	9 + 6	1 + 2	5 + 9	2 + 8
6 + 4	8 + 7	0 + 6	7 + 6	1 + 7	3 + 7	9 + 0	4 + 7	0 + 2	5 + 3
2 + 2	2 + 0	3 + 9	5 + 5	3 + 5	0 + 5	7 + 7	2 + 6	3 + 8	4 + 0
9 + 1	9 + 4	5 + 2	1 + 0	8 + 2	6 + 3	4 + 2	7 + 1	1 + 1	8 + 5

3-77Fa

Name _____ •

(Draw an 80 mm line segment.)

Date _____ •

(Draw a line segment 10 mm shorter than the line segment for your name.)

1. The high temperatures yesterday in Boston, Bismarck, Raleigh, and Denver were 45°F, 15°F, 58°F, and 37°F, respectively. Write the names of the cities and their temperatures in order from coldest to warmest.

   _____   _____   _____   _____

   _____°F   _____°F   _____°F   _____°F

   How much warmer was it in Boston than in Bismark? _____

2. Each large square is one cake.
   Label the size of each piece.

   The children in Room 3 ate $1\frac{1}{2}$ cakes.
   Color the amount they ate.

3. Write $53.25 as you would on a check.

   _____ DOLLARS

4. Each cup has 10 dimes. There are 3 cups.
   Draw a picture to show the dimes in the cups.
   Write a number sentence to match the picture.

   _____

   How much money is that altogether? _____

5. In the morning, Mrs. Ritter told the children that they would have a special visitor 2 hours from now. The clock shows the time now.

   At what time will the visitor arrive? _____

6. Use the correct comparison symbol (>, <, or =).

   400 ÷ 10 ☐ 9 × 4 + 10   530 − 300 ☐ 23 × 10   7 × 7 ☐ 19 + 28

Name _____

Date _____

1. The high temperatures yesterday in Jackson, Austin, Carson City, and Des Moines were 73°F, 78°F, 42°F, and 40°F, respectively. Write the names of the cities and their temperatures in order from coldest to warmest.

   _____   _____   _____   _____

   _____°F   _____°F   _____°F   _____°F

   How much colder was it in Des Moines than in Austin? _____

2. Each circle is one pie.
   Label the size of each piece.

   The Taylor family ate $1\frac{1}{3}$ pies.
   Color the amount they ate.

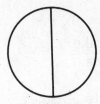  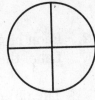

3. Write $68.37 as you would on a check.

   _____ DOLLARS

4. Each cup has 5 nickels. There are 4 cups. Draw a picture to show the nickels in the cups. Write a number sentence to match the picture.

   _____

   How much money is that altogether? _____

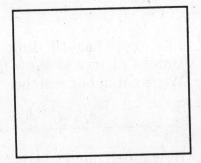

5. In the afternoon, Mrs. Miller told the children that the principal would visit the class 1 hour from now. The clock shows the time now.

   At what time will the principal arrive? _____

6. Use the correct comparison symbol (>, <, or =).

   8×7 ☐ $600 \div 10$ $607 - 500$ ☐ $70 + 60$ $6 \times 4 + 30$ ☐ $27 + 27$

12	17	11	10	15
− 9	− 9	− 9	− 9	− 9

9	13	16	12	14
− 9	− 9	− 9	− 9	− 9

18	13	9	15	11
− 9	− 9	− 9	− 9	− 9

10	17	14	12	13
− 9	− 9	− 9	− 9	− 9

16	11	18	15	12
− 9	− 9	− 9	− 9	− 9

Score: _____

3-78Fa

4 × 4	4 × 10	1 × 4	8 × 4	4 × 3
4 × 5	4 × 9	6 × 4	2 × 4	4 × 7
0 × 4	6 × 4	4 × 4	2 × 4	4 × 9
4 × 7	4 × 5	4 × 1	8 × 4	3 × 4
4 × 10	3 × 4	4 × 5	7 × 4	4 × 0

Score: _____

Name •
    (Draw a 2" line segment.)

Date •

(Draw a congruent line segment. It is _____ mm long. Write the date using digits.)

1. Roger had some money. His sister gave him 35¢. Now he has 97¢. How much money did he have before?

   Number sentence _____

   Answer _____

2. I have 4 one-dollar bills and 7 hundred-dollar bills.

   How much money is this? _____

3. Write $26.05 as you would on a check.

   _____ DOLLARS

4. Write the first ten perfect squares.

   _____, _____, _____, _____, _____, _____, _____, _____, _____, _____

   Circle the even numbers.

5. Find each difference.

16	12	18	11	15	13	17	14
− 9	− 9	− 9	− 9	− 9	− 9	− 9	− 9

6. Draw a pictograph to show the following information.

   Books Read
   Duane   35 books
   Elliot   49 books
   Chris   21 books

   BOOKS READ

Duane	
Elliot	
Chris	

   ☐ = 7 books

7. What are the smudged digits?

   93 − $\blacksquare$0 = 63 $\blacksquare$ × 4 = 6 × 6   25 + 6$\blacksquare$ = 90

   ___   ___   ___

Name _____

Date _____

1. Courtney had some money. Her brother gave her 40¢. Now she has 95¢. How much money did she have before?

   Number sentence _____

   Answer _____

2. I have 6 ten-dollar bills and 3 hundred-dollar bills.

   How much money is this? _____

3. Write $42.01 as you would on a check.

   _____ DOLLARS

4. Count by 4's. Write the numbers.

   _____, _____, _____, _____, _____, _____, _____, _____, _____, _____

   Circle the even numbers.

5. Find each difference.

12	15	18	11	14	17	13	16
− 9	− 9	− 9	− 9	− 9	− 9	− 9	− 9

6. Draw a pictograph to show the following information.

   Books Read
   Corry   30 books
   Tanya   40 books
   Verna   25 books

   BOOKS READ

Corry	
Tanya	
Verna	

   □ = 5 books

7. What are the smudged digits?

   $85 - \blacksquare 0 = 35$ $4 \times 3 = 2 \times \blacksquare$ $57 + 2\blacksquare = 80$

   ___   ___   ___

3-78Wb

MASTER1

Name _____

Today's Date is _____

Today's Pattern
_____
_____

Coin Cup

Q	D	N	P	Total Coins

Today's Problem
_____

Today's Date is _____

Today's Pattern
_____
_____

Coin Cup

Q	D	N	P	Total Coins

Today's Problem
_____

Today's Date is _____

Today's Pattern
_____
_____

Coin Cup

Q	D	N	P	Total Coins

Today's Problem
_____

Today's Date is _____

Today's Pattern
_____
_____

Coin Cup

Q	D	N	P	Total Coins

Today's Problem
_____

Today's Date is _____

Today's Pattern
_____
_____

Coin Cup

Q	D	N	P	Total Coins

Today's Problem
_____

12 − 9	17 − 9	11 − 9	10 − 9	15 − 9
9 − 9	13 − 9	16 − 9	12 − 9	14 − 9
18 − 9	13 − 9	9 − 9	15 − 9	11 − 9
10 − 9	17 − 9	14 − 9	12 − 9	13 − 9
16 − 9	11 − 9	18 − 9	15 − 9	12 − 9

Score: _____

$$\begin{array}{r} 8 \\ \times\ 5 \\ \hline \end{array} \qquad \begin{array}{r} 4 \\ \times\ 4 \\ \hline \end{array} \qquad \begin{array}{r} 2 \\ \times\ 8 \\ \hline \end{array} \qquad \begin{array}{r} 4 \\ \times\ 9 \\ \hline \end{array} \qquad \begin{array}{r} 3 \\ \times\ 4 \\ \hline \end{array}$$

$$\begin{array}{r} 7 \\ \times\ 7 \\ \hline \end{array} \qquad \begin{array}{r} 4 \\ \times\ 8 \\ \hline \end{array} \qquad \begin{array}{r} 5 \\ \times\ 4 \\ \hline \end{array} \qquad \begin{array}{r} 3 \\ \times\ 10 \\ \hline \end{array} \qquad \begin{array}{r} 4 \\ \times\ 2 \\ \hline \end{array}$$

$$\begin{array}{r} 7 \\ \times\ 4 \\ \hline \end{array} \qquad \begin{array}{r} 4 \\ \times\ 10 \\ \hline \end{array} \qquad \begin{array}{r} 1 \\ \times\ 6 \\ \hline \end{array} \qquad \begin{array}{r} 5 \\ \times\ 9 \\ \hline \end{array} \qquad \begin{array}{r} 6 \\ \times\ 4 \\ \hline \end{array}$$

$$\begin{array}{r} 3 \\ \times\ 2 \\ \hline \end{array} \qquad \begin{array}{r} 9 \\ \times\ 4 \\ \hline \end{array} \qquad \begin{array}{r} 6 \\ \times\ 7 \\ \hline \end{array} \qquad \begin{array}{r} 4 \\ \times\ 0 \\ \hline \end{array} \qquad \begin{array}{r} 10 \\ \times\ 8 \\ \hline \end{array}$$

$$\begin{array}{r} 1 \\ \times\ 4 \\ \hline \end{array} \qquad \begin{array}{r} 4 \\ \times\ 8 \\ \hline \end{array} \qquad \begin{array}{r} 5 \\ \times\ 3 \\ \hline \end{array} \qquad \begin{array}{r} 4 \\ \times\ 6 \\ \hline \end{array} \qquad \begin{array}{r} 7 \\ \times\ 8 \\ \hline \end{array}$$

Score: _____

3-79Fb

Name •

     (Draw a 94 mm line segment.)

Date •

     (Draw a $1\frac{1}{2}''$ line segment. Write the date using digits.)

1. Roseann had $1.75 in quarters. How many quarters did she have? _____
She gave Frank 5 quarters.
How much money does Roseann have now? _____

2. Use the digit cards to make the following numbers.

the largest 3-digit number _____

the smallest 3-digit number _____

the 3-digit number closest to 500 _____

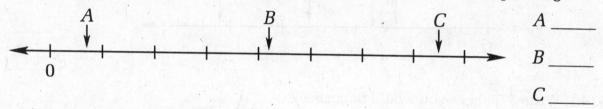

3. Number the number line by 10's. Approximately where is each arrow pointing?

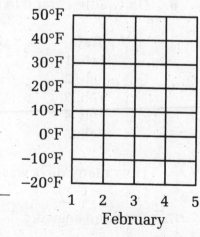

A _____

B _____

C _____

4. Write $92.17 as you would on a check.

_____ DOLLARS

5. Simplify.

$\sqrt{64}$ = _____ $\sqrt{25}$ = _____ $\sqrt{36}$ = _____ $\sqrt{4}$ = _____

6. Draw a line graph to show the following temperatures.

Date	Temperatures
Feb. 1	28°F
Feb. 2	17°F
Feb. 3	34°F
Feb. 4	−10°F
Feb. 5	5°F

How many days was the temperature above freezing? _____

50°F
40°F
30°F
20°F
10°F
0°F
−10°F
−20°F

1   2   3   4   5
February

7. Find the answers.

49 + 26 = _____   35 + 47 = _____
$\begin{array}{r} 17 \\ -\ 9 \\ \hline \end{array}$
$\begin{array}{r} 12 \\ -\ 9 \\ \hline \end{array}$
$\begin{array}{r} 15 \\ -\ 9 \\ \hline \end{array}$

1. Evan had $1.25 in quarters. How many quarters did he have? _____
    He gave Roy 2 quarters.
    How much money does Evan have now? _____

2. Use the digit cards to make the following numbers.

    the largest 3-digit number _____

    the smallest 3-digit number _____

    the 3-digit number closest to 500 _____

    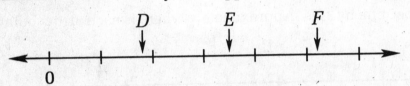

3. Number the number line by 10's. Approximately where is each arrow pointing?

    D E F

    0

    D _____

    E _____

    F _____

4. Write $75.04 as you would on a check.

    _____ DOLLARS

5. Simplify.

    $\sqrt{16}$ = ____ $\sqrt{81}$ = ____ $\sqrt{100}$ = ____ $\sqrt{9}$ = ____

6. Draw a line graph to show the following temperatures.

Date	Temperatures
Feb. 1	12°F
Feb. 2	43°F
Feb. 3	35°F
Feb. 4	0°F
Feb. 5	17°F

    50°F
    40°F
    30°F
    20°F
    10°F
    0°F
    −10°F
    −20°F
    1   2   3   4   5
    February

    How many days was the temperature below freezing? _____

7. Find the answers.

    $27 + 56 = $ ____ $48 + 38 = $ ____ $\begin{array}{r} 16 \\ -\ 9 \\ \hline \end{array}$ $\begin{array}{r} 11 \\ -\ 9 \\ \hline \end{array}$ $\begin{array}{r} 14 \\ -\ 9 \\ \hline \end{array}$

Name _____

Bag _____

1. Do not look inside the bag.
   Take one tile out of the bag.
   Tally the color of the tile you drew.
   Put the tile back in the bag and mix the tiles.
   Do this 80 times.

red	
yellow	
blue	
green	

2. Make a bar graph showing the number of color tiles you tallied.

red								
yellow								
blue								
green								

          10   20   30   40   50   60   70   80

3. Write four things you notice about the graph. _____

   _____

   _____

   _____

   _____

There are 8 tiles in the bag. How many tiles of each color do you think are in the bag?

_____ red _____ yellow _____ blue _____ green

$$\begin{array}{r} 12 \\ -\ 9 \\ \hline \end{array} \qquad \begin{array}{r} 17 \\ -\ 9 \\ \hline \end{array} \qquad \begin{array}{r} 11 \\ -\ 9 \\ \hline \end{array} \qquad \begin{array}{r} 10 \\ -\ 9 \\ \hline \end{array} \qquad \begin{array}{r} 15 \\ -\ 9 \\ \hline \end{array}$$

$$\begin{array}{r} 9 \\ -\ 9 \\ \hline \end{array} \qquad \begin{array}{r} 13 \\ -\ 9 \\ \hline \end{array} \qquad \begin{array}{r} 16 \\ -\ 9 \\ \hline \end{array} \qquad \begin{array}{r} 12 \\ -\ 9 \\ \hline \end{array} \qquad \begin{array}{r} 14 \\ -\ 9 \\ \hline \end{array}$$

$$\begin{array}{r} 18 \\ -\ 9 \\ \hline \end{array} \qquad \begin{array}{r} 13 \\ -\ 9 \\ \hline \end{array} \qquad \begin{array}{r} 9 \\ -\ 9 \\ \hline \end{array} \qquad \begin{array}{r} 15 \\ -\ 9 \\ \hline \end{array} \qquad \begin{array}{r} 11 \\ -\ 9 \\ \hline \end{array}$$

$$\begin{array}{r} 10 \\ -\ 9 \\ \hline \end{array} \qquad \begin{array}{r} 17 \\ -\ 9 \\ \hline \end{array} \qquad \begin{array}{r} 14 \\ -\ 9 \\ \hline \end{array} \qquad \begin{array}{r} 12 \\ -\ 9 \\ \hline \end{array} \qquad \begin{array}{r} 13 \\ -\ 9 \\ \hline \end{array}$$

$$\begin{array}{r} 16 \\ -\ 9 \\ \hline \end{array} \qquad \begin{array}{r} 11 \\ -\ 9 \\ \hline \end{array} \qquad \begin{array}{r} 18 \\ -\ 9 \\ \hline \end{array} \qquad \begin{array}{r} 15 \\ -\ 9 \\ \hline \end{array} \qquad \begin{array}{r} 12 \\ -\ 9 \\ \hline \end{array}$$

Score: _____

1. It takes Shawna an hour to walk to school. She leaves her house at 7:40 each morning.

   At what time does she arrive at school? _____

2. Frank had some money. His brother gave him 30¢. Now he has 55¢. How much money did he have before?

   Number sentence _____ Answer _____

3. Put these numbers in order from smallest to largest: | 124   79   120   75   93 |

   _____ _____ _____ _____ _____

4. Use these digit cards to make the following numbers. Use each digit card only once for each number. | 2 | 5 | 7 |

   largest number _____   smallest number _____   number closest to 500 _____

5. Draw 6 groups of 4 quarters.

   Write a number sentence for the picture.

   _____

   How many quarters did you draw? _____

   How much money is this? _____

6. Write these numbers using digits.

   four hundred seventy _____

   two hundred fifty-three _____

   five hundred four _____

7. Mrs. Holt's class ate $3\frac{1}{4}$ pizzas.

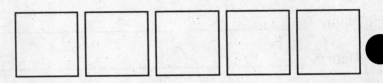

Shade the pizzas to show
how much they ate.

Circle the fraction that shows how much pizza is left. $1\frac{1}{4}$, $1\frac{2}{4}$, $1\frac{3}{4}$, 1, $\frac{1}{4}$

8. List the first 10 perfect squares.

_____ , _____ , _____ , _____ , _____ , _____ , _____ , _____ , _____ , _____

Circle the odd numbers.

9. Find the answers.

46 + 28 = _____   97 − 40 = _____   600 ÷ 10 = _____

27 + 27 = _____   63 − 50 = _____   48 × 10 = _____

243 + 300 = _____   430 − 200 = _____   10 × 25 = _____

2 + 6 + 3 + 9 + 4 + 8 + 7 + 1 + 8 + 5 + 1 = _____

10. Use the graph to answer the questions.

Shade the graph to show
that team D scored 14 points.

How many points did
teams A and C score together? _____

About how many
points did team B score? _____

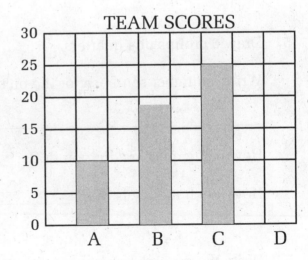

$$
\begin{array}{r} 8 \\ \times\,5 \\ \hline \end{array}
\qquad
\begin{array}{r} 4 \\ \times\,4 \\ \hline \end{array}
\qquad
\begin{array}{r} 2 \\ \times\,8 \\ \hline \end{array}
\qquad
\begin{array}{r} 4 \\ \times\,9 \\ \hline \end{array}
\qquad
\begin{array}{r} 3 \\ \times\,4 \\ \hline \end{array}
$$

$$
\begin{array}{r} 7 \\ \times\,7 \\ \hline \end{array}
\qquad
\begin{array}{r} 4 \\ \times\,8 \\ \hline \end{array}
\qquad
\begin{array}{r} 5 \\ \times\,4 \\ \hline \end{array}
\qquad
\begin{array}{r} 3 \\ \times\,10 \\ \hline \end{array}
\qquad
\begin{array}{r} 4 \\ \times\,2 \\ \hline \end{array}
$$

$$
\begin{array}{r} 7 \\ \times\,4 \\ \hline \end{array}
\qquad
\begin{array}{r} 4 \\ \times\,10 \\ \hline \end{array}
\qquad
\begin{array}{r} 1 \\ \times\,6 \\ \hline \end{array}
\qquad
\begin{array}{r} 5 \\ \times\,9 \\ \hline \end{array}
\qquad
\begin{array}{r} 6 \\ \times\,4 \\ \hline \end{array}
$$

$$
\begin{array}{r} 3 \\ \times\,2 \\ \hline \end{array}
\qquad
\begin{array}{r} 9 \\ \times\,4 \\ \hline \end{array}
\qquad
\begin{array}{r} 6 \\ \times\,7 \\ \hline \end{array}
\qquad
\begin{array}{r} 4 \\ \times\,0 \\ \hline \end{array}
\qquad
\begin{array}{r} 10 \\ \times\,8 \\ \hline \end{array}
$$

$$
\begin{array}{r} 1 \\ \times\,4 \\ \hline \end{array}
\qquad
\begin{array}{r} 4 \\ \times\,8 \\ \hline \end{array}
\qquad
\begin{array}{r} 5 \\ \times\,3 \\ \hline \end{array}
\qquad
\begin{array}{r} 4 \\ \times\,6 \\ \hline \end{array}
\qquad
\begin{array}{r} 7 \\ \times\,8 \\ \hline \end{array}
$$

Score: _____

Name •
    (Draw an 8 cm 9 mm line segment.)

Date •

    (Draw a 42 mm line segment.)

1. Serina baby-sits once a week. She baby-sits for three hours each time. How many hours will Serina baby-sit in four weeks?

   Number sentence _____ Answer _____

2. Mrs. Meyers bought a dozen eggs. Draw the eggs. She used 3 eggs to make a cake. Cross out the eggs she used.

   What fractional part of the eggs did she use? _____

   What fractional part of the eggs does she have left? _____

3. Show **9:55** on the clock.

   It's morning.
   What time will it be 3 hours from now? _____

4. Use the correct comparison symbol (>, <, or =).

   $\sqrt{49}$ ☐ 16 − 9   3 × 4 − 4 ☐ $\sqrt{81}$ 15 × 10 ☐ 420 − 300

5. Find each sum.

   $627.00 $183.00 $317.00
   + 281.00   + 409.00   + 87.00

6. Complete the patterns. Find the rules.

   ____, ____, ____, 43, 48, 53, ____, ____, ____   Rule: ____

   ____, ____, ____, ____, ____, ____, 294, 292, 290   Rule: ____

Name _____

Date _____

1. Russell helps his father after school on Wednesdays. He helps him for two hours each Wednesday. How many hours will Russell help his father in four weeks?

   Number sentence _____ Answer _____

2. Ann Marie bought a half dozen dog bones for her dog. Draw the dog bones. The dog ate 2 the first day. Cross them out.

   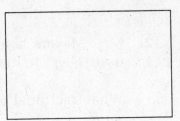

   What fractional part of the dog
   bones did the dog eat the first day? _____

   What fractional part of the dog bones are left? _____

3. Show **4:35** on the clock.

   It's afternoon.
   What time will it be 4 hours from now? _____

4. Use the correct comparison symbol (>, <, or =).

   $15 - 9$ ☐ $\sqrt{64}$ $90 \div 10$ ☐ $\sqrt{81}$ $\sqrt{36}$ ☐ $6 \times 4 - 20$

5. Find each sum.

   $593.00
   + 252.00
   _____

   $254.00
   + 30.00
   _____

   $195.00
   + 245.00
   _____

6. Complete the patterns. Find the rules.

   _____, _____, _____, 405, 410, 415, _____, _____, _____   Rule: _____

   _____, _____, _____, _____, _____, _____, 64, 59, 54   Rule: _____

Name _____

Date _____

PAY TO THE
ORDER OF _____ $ [   ]

_____ DOLLARS

_____

Date _____

PAY TO THE
ORDER OF _____ $ [   ]

_____ DOLLARS

_____

Date _____

PAY TO THE
ORDER OF _____ $ [   ]

_____ DOLLARS

_____

12 − 9	16 − 7	17 − 9	13 − 4	15 − 9
14 − 5	13 − 9	17 − 8	16 − 9	11 − 9
18 − 9	16 − 7	10 − 9	14 − 9	12 − 3
9 − 9	15 − 6	17 − 8	16 − 7	13 − 9
15 − 9	12 − 3	14 − 5	17 − 9	13 − 4

Score: _____

Name _____

M 15.2

```
   8        4        2        4        3
 × 5      × 4      × 8      × 9      × 4
 ───      ───      ───      ───      ───

   7        4        5        3        4
 × 7      × 8      × 4      ×10      × 2
 ───      ───      ───      ───      ───

   7        4        1        5        6
 × 4      ×10      × 6      × 9      × 4
 ───      ───      ───      ───      ───

   3        9        6        4       10
 × 2      × 4      × 7      × 0      × 8
 ───      ───      ───      ───      ───

   1        4        5        4        7
 × 4      × 8      × 3      × 6      × 8
 ───      ───      ───      ───      ───
```

Score: _____

3-82Fb

Name
(Draw a $4\frac{1}{2}''$ line segment.)

Date

(Draw a 78 mm line segment. It is _____ cm _____ mm long.)

1. Sandy drew a picture on an 8-inch by 10-inch piece of paper. She wants to put ribbon along the edge to make a border. Draw a small sketch of the picture. How many inches of ribbon will she need?

    Number sentence _____

    Answer _____

2. Write $728.81 as you would on a check.

    _____ DOLLARS

3. Write a number sentence for each of these pictures (☺ = cookie).

    A. 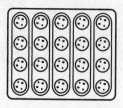   B. 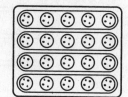   C.

    _____   _____   _____

    Which picture shows how 4 children will share the cookies? _____

    How many cookies will each child have? _____

4. Find the sums.

    ```
      $263.00          $492.00          $356.00
    + 718.00         + 258.00         +  76.00
    ```

5. What are the smudged digits?

    6▮ + 17 = 80   ▮ × 4 = 3 × 4 + 12   3▮0 − 200 = 140

    ___   ___   ___

6. Use a scrap piece of paper. Follow these directions.
    (1) Draw an 80 mm horizontal line segment near the bottom edge of the paper.
    (2) Draw 60 mm vertical line segments up from each endpoint.
    (3) Connect the top endpoints of the vertical line segments.

    What shape did you make? _____   What is the perimeter? _____

Name _____

Date _____

1. William made a birthday card for his mother. The card is 4 inches by 6 inches. He wants to put lace along the edge to make a border. Draw a small sketch of the card. How many inches of lace will he need?

   Number sentence _____

   Answer _____

2. Write $679.04 as you would on a check.

   _____ DOLLARS

3. Write a number sentence for each of these pictures. (☺ = cookie)

   A.    B. ☺☺☺☺ / ☺☺☺ / ☺☺☺☺   C.

   _____   _____   _____

   Which picture shows how 3 children will share the cookies? _____

   How many cookies will each child have? _____

4. Find the sums.

   $452.00 $716.00 $563.00
   + 339.00   + 136.00   + 98.00
   _____   _____   _____

5. What are the smudged digits?

   5▪ + 16 = 70   ▪ × 4 = 5 × 4 + 8   5▪0 − 300 = 270

   ___   ___   ___

6. Ask someone at home to let you count the change in their pocket or wallet. Record the number of coins and the total amount of money.

Q	D	N	P	Total Coins

   Total amount _____

Name _____

Today's Date is _____

Today's Pattern _____

_____

Today's Problem _____

Coin Cup

Q	D'	N	P	Total Coins

Today's Date is _____

Today's Pattern _____

_____

Today's Problem _____

Coin Cup

Q	D	N	P	Total Coins

Today's Date is _____

Today's Pattern _____

_____

Today's Problem _____

Coin Cup

Q	D	N	P	Total Coins

Today's Date is _____

Today's Pattern _____

_____

Today's Problem _____

Coin Cup

Q	D	N	P	Total Coins

Today's Date is _____

Today's Pattern _____

_____

Today's Problem _____

Coin Cup

Q	D	N	P	Total Coins

January 2000

S	M	T	W	T	F	S
						1
2	3	4	5	6	7	8
9	10	11	12	13	14	15
16	17	18	19	20	21	22
23	24	25	26	27	28	29
30	31					

February 2000

S	M	T	W	T	F	S
		1	2	3	4	5
6	7	8	9	10	11	12
13	14	15	16	17	18	19
20	21	22	23	24	25	26
27	28	29				

March 2000

S	M	T	W	T	F	S
			1	2	3	4
5	6	7	8	9	10	11
12	13	14	15	16	17	18
19	20	21	22	23	24	25
26	27	28	29	30	31	

April 2000

S	M	T	W	T	F	S
						1
2	3	4	5	6	7	8
9	10	11	12	13	14	15
16	17	18	19	20	21	22
23	24	25	26	27	28	29
30						

May 2000

S	M	T	W	T	F	S
	1	2	3	4	5	6
7	8	9	10	11	12	13
14	15	16	17	18	19	20
21	22	23	24	25	26	27
28	29	30	31			

June 2000

S	M	T	W	T	F	S
				1	2	3
4	5	6	7	8	9	10
11	12	13	14	15	16	17
18	19	20	21	22	23	24
25	26	27	28	29	30	

July 2000

S	M	T	W	T	F	S
						1
2	3	4	5	6	7	8
9	10	11	12	13	14	15
16	17	18	19	20	21	22
23	24	25	26	27	28	29
30	31					

August 2000

S	M	T	W	T	F	S
		1	2	3	4	5
6	7	8	9	10	11	12
13	14	15	16	17	18	19
20	21	22	23	24	25	26
27	28	29	30	31		

September 2000

S	M	T	W	T	F	S
					1	2
3	4	5	6	7	8	9
10	11	12	13	14	15	16
17	18	19	20	21	22	23
24	25	26	27	28	29	30

October 2000

S	M	T	W	T	F	S
1	2	3	4	5	6	7
8	9	10	11	12	13	14
15	16	17	18	19	20	21
22	23	24	25	26	27	28
29	30	31				

November 2000

S	M	T	W	T	F	S
			1	2	3	4
5	6	7	8	9	10	11
12	13	14	15	16	17	18
19	20	21	22	23	24	25
26	27	28	29	30		

December 2000

S	M	T	W	T	F	S
					1	2
3	4	5	6	7	8	9
10	11	12	13	14	15	16
17	18	19	20	21	22	23
24	25	26	27	28	29	30
31						

12 − 9	16 − 7	17 − 9	13 − 4	15 − 9
14 − 5	13 − 9	17 − 8	16 − 9	11 − 9
18 − 9	16 − 7	10 − 9	14 − 9	12 − 3
9 − 9	15 − 6	17 − 8	16 − 7	13 − 9
15 − 9	12 − 3	14 − 5	17 − 9	13 − 4

Score: _____

3-83Fa

Name _____   Score: _____   **A2-100**

5 + 4	4 + 6	2 + 3	6 + 8	5 + 0	0 + 9	4 + 8	5 + 6	1 + 3	6 + 1
2 + 5	0 + 8	6 + 7	0 + 3	2 + 9	8 + 8	6 + 0	1 + 9	6 + 9	8 + 4
1 + 6	9 + 8	1 + 5	4 + 9	8 + 6	2 + 4	7 + 9	8 + 3	4 + 3	0 + 4
7 + 3	3 + 2	7 + 0	7 + 2	1 + 4	6 + 5	3 + 6	3 + 0	8 + 0	9 + 7
9 + 9	7 + 8	7 + 4	9 + 5	5 + 7	1 + 8	0 + 1	8 + 9	2 + 7	7 + 5
0 + 7	6 + 6	3 + 3	2 + 6	6 + 2	9 + 2	5 + 8	4 + 5	9 + 3	3 + 1
5 + 1	4 + 1	8 + 1	3 + 4	0 + 0	4 + 4	9 + 6	1 + 2	5 + 9	2 + 8
6 + 4	8 + 7	0 + 6	7 + 6	1 + 7	3 + 7	9 + 0	4 + 7	0 + 2	5 + 3
2 + 2	2 + 0	3 + 9	5 + 5	3 + 5	0 + 5	7 + 7	2 + 6	3 + 8	4 + 0
9 + 1	9 + 4	5 + 2	1 + 0	8 + 2	6 + 3	4 + 2	7 + 1	1 + 1	8 + 5

3-83Fb

Name •
(Draw an 8 cm 3 mm line segment.)

Date •

(Draw a line segment 10 mm longer than your name line segment.)

1. There are 4 markers in a small package. The medium size package has twice that amount. The large size package has five times as many as the small size.

    How many markers are in the medium package? _____

    How many markers are in the large package? _____

2. There are a half dozen people in line. You are fourth.

    How many people are before you? _____   How many people are after you? _____

3. Write $823.15 as you would on a check.

    _____ DOLLARS

4. Find each sum.

    $237.00 + $328.00 $528.00 + $394.00 $175.00 + $46.00

5. Circle the fraction which is closest to 1. Shade the cups to show that you are correct.

    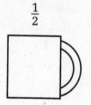   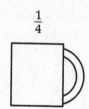   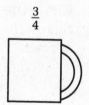

6. How much money does each child have?

    Ramona: 5 quarters, 2 nickels _____   Dora: 9 dimes, 8 nickels _____

    Billy: 3 quarters, 7 dimes _____   Felix: 4 quarters, 8 nickels _____

    Write the names of the children in order from the one who has the most money to the one who has the least.

    _____   _____   _____   _____

Name _____
Date _____

1. There are 5 stickers in a small package. The medium size package has twice that amount. The large size package has four times as many as the small size.

   How many stickers are in the medium package? _____

   How many stickers are in the large package? _____

2. There are two dozen people in line. You are third.

   How many people are before you? _____   How many people are after you? _____

3. Write $792.31 as you would on a check.

   _____ Dollars

4. Find each sum.

   $342.00 + $409.00 $727.00 + $194.00 $249.00 + $37.00

5. Circle the fraction that is closest to 1. Shade the cups to show that you are correct.

   $\frac{1}{3}$ $\frac{2}{3}$ $\frac{1}{2}$

   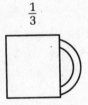 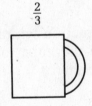 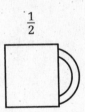

6. How much money does each child have?

   Cathy: 2 quarters, 6 nickels _____   Greg: 1 quarter, 10 dimes _____

   Danny: 3 quarters, 3 dimes _____   Heather: 4 quarters, 3 nickels _____

   Write the names of the children in order from the one who has the most money to the one who has the least.

   _____   _____   _____   _____

Name _____

¢

Quarters	Dimes	Nickels	Pennies	Total Coins

3-84Ma

12 − 9	16 − 7	17 − 9	13 − 4	15 − 9
14 − 5	13 − 9	17 − 8	16 − 9	11 − 9
18 − 9	16 − 7	10 − 9	14 − 9	12 − 3
9 − 9	15 − 6	17 − 8	16 − 7	13 − 9
15 − 9	12 − 3	14 − 5	17 − 9	13 − 4

Score: _____

Name ∙

(Draw a 90 mm line segment.)

Date ∙

(Draw a line segment 2 cm longer than your name line segment.)

1. It takes Mrs. Eagan two hours to drive to the airport. What is the latest time she can leave in order to be at the airport by 7:00 a.m.? _____

2. Write 493 using words. _____

Write seven hundred ninety using digits. _____

3. Draw a line graph to show the following temperatures.

Date	Temperature
Feb. 21	8°F
Feb. 22	−10°F
Feb. 23	12°F
Feb. 24	−5°F
Feb. 25	39°F

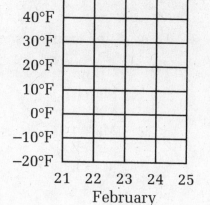

4. What is the length of the rectangle in millimeters? _____ mm

What is the width of the rectangle in millimeters? _____ mm

What is the perimeter of the rectangle in millimeters? _____ mm

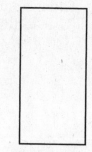

5. How many days are in each of the following months?

May _____   August _____   September _____   March _____

How many days are in one year? _____

6. Find the sums.

$$\begin{array}{r} \$2\,4\,7\,.\,0\,0 \\ +\,3\,9\,2\,.\,0\,0 \\ \hline \end{array}$$

$658.00 + $163.00

$39.00 + $447.00

7. What are the smudged digits?

$4\blacklozenge + 14 = 60$ $4 \times \blacklozenge = 80 \div 10$ $93 - \blacklozenge0 = 53$ $16 - \blacklozenge = \sqrt{49}$

___   ___   ___   ___

Name _____

Date _____

1. It takes Marvin one hour to walk to school. What is the latest time he can leave in order to be at school by 8:30 a.m.? _____

2. Write 624 using words. _____

   Write five hundred sixty using digits. _____

3. Draw a line graph to show the following temperatures.

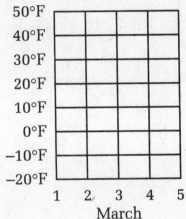

Date	Temperature
March 1	18°F
March 2	−11°F
March 3	−15°F
March 4	5°F
March 5	23°F

4. Today's number is _____. Write 4 number sentences.
   (Use addition, subtraction, multiplication, and division.)

   _____ _____ _____ _____

5. How many days are in each of the following months?

   January _____   April _____   October _____   November _____

   How many days are in a leap year? _____

6. Find the sums.

   $$\begin{array}{r} \$9\,2\,4\,.\,0\,0 \\ +\quad 6\,8\,.\,0\,0 \\ \hline \end{array}$$
   $42.00 + $285.00 $259.00 + $373.00

7. What are the smudged digits?

   $59 + 2\blacksquare = 80$ $4 \times \blacksquare = 200 \div 10$ $67 - \blacksquare 0 = 47$ $15 - \blacksquare = \sqrt{36}$

   ___   ___   ___   ___

Name •
    (Draw a 9 cm 2 mm line segment.)

Date •
    (Draw a 65 mm line segment.)

1. The children in Room 17 collected 47 cans. The children in Room 15 collected 35 cans. How many cans did the children in the two rooms collect altogether?

   Number sentence _____ Answer _____

2. Sheena had some quarters. Calvin gave her 9 more quarters. Now she has 16 quarters. How many quarters did she have before?

   Number sentence _____ Answer _____

3. Draw a graph to match this chart.

   FAVORITE DAY

Day	Friday	Saturday	Sunday
Number of Children	8	13	7

   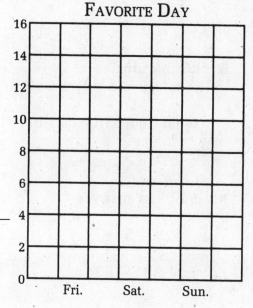

   FAVORITE DAY

   How many children chose a weekend day? _____

   How many more children
   chose Friday than chose Sunday? _____

4. There are a dozen people in line. You are ninth.

   How many people are before you? _____

   How many people are after you? _____

5. Write these numbers using words.

   68 _____

   54 _____

3-85Aa

6. Draw a half dozen cupcakes.

   Put green frosting on 2 of the cupcakes.
   Put red frosting on the rest of the cupcakes.

   What fractional part of the
   cupcakes has green frosting? _____

   What fractional part of the
   cupcakes has red frosting? _____

7. Circle the combinations of coins that equal 57¢.

   2 quarters, 1 dime, 2 pennies   4 dimes, 3 nickels, 2 pennies

   1 quarter, 3 dimes, 2 pennies   1 quarter, 5 nickels, 7 pennies

8. It's morning.
   What time is shown on the clock? _____

   What time will it be 1 hour from now? _____

   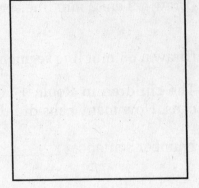

9. Find the answers.

   2 + 5 + 3 + 7 + 1 + 2 + 9 + 4 + 8 + 6 = _____

   39 + 53 = _____   16 + 74 = _____   23 + 45 = _____

   6 × 4 = _____   8 × 8 = _____   9 × 5 = _____

   300 ÷ 10 = _____   42 × 10 = _____   340 − 100 = _____

10. Complete the number patterns. Write the rules.

   _____ , _____ , _____ , 580, 585, 590, _____ , _____ , _____   Rule: _____

   250, 275, 300, _____ , _____ , _____ , _____ , _____ , _____   Rule: _____

   457, 455, 453, _____ , _____ , _____ , _____ , _____ , _____   Rule: _____

$$\begin{array}{r} 5 \\ \times\ 8 \\ \hline \end{array} \qquad \begin{array}{r} 8 \\ \times\ 1 \\ \hline \end{array} \qquad \begin{array}{r} 8 \\ \times\ 7 \\ \hline \end{array} \qquad \begin{array}{r} 2 \\ \times\ 8 \\ \hline \end{array} \qquad \begin{array}{r} 4 \\ \times\ 8 \\ \hline \end{array}$$

$$\begin{array}{r} 8 \\ \times\ 8 \\ \hline \end{array} \qquad \begin{array}{r} 8 \\ \times\ 0 \\ \hline \end{array} \qquad \begin{array}{r} 8 \\ \times\ 6 \\ \hline \end{array} \qquad \begin{array}{r} 3 \\ \times\ 8 \\ \hline \end{array} \qquad \begin{array}{r} 9 \\ \times\ 8 \\ \hline \end{array}$$

$$\begin{array}{r} 1 \\ \times\ 8 \\ \hline \end{array} \qquad \begin{array}{r} 8 \\ \times\ 8 \\ \hline \end{array} \qquad \begin{array}{r} 5 \\ \times\ 8 \\ \hline \end{array} \qquad \begin{array}{r} 8 \\ \times\ 2 \\ \hline \end{array} \qquad \begin{array}{r} 3 \\ \times\ 8 \\ \hline \end{array}$$

$$\begin{array}{r} 8 \\ \times\ 4 \\ \hline \end{array} \qquad \begin{array}{r} 8 \\ \times\ 9 \\ \hline \end{array} \qquad \begin{array}{r} 0 \\ \times\ 8 \\ \hline \end{array} \qquad \begin{array}{r} 6 \\ \times\ 8 \\ \hline \end{array} \qquad \begin{array}{r} 8 \\ \times\ 7 \\ \hline \end{array}$$

$$\begin{array}{r} 8 \\ \times\ 3 \\ \hline \end{array} \qquad \begin{array}{r} 2 \\ \times\ 8 \\ \hline \end{array} \qquad \begin{array}{r} 9 \\ \times\ 8 \\ \hline \end{array} \qquad \begin{array}{r} 4 \\ \times\ 8 \\ \hline \end{array} \qquad \begin{array}{r} 8 \\ \times\ 6 \\ \hline \end{array}$$

Score: _____

3-85Fa

Name ●
(Draw an 8 cm 7 mm line segment.)

Date ●

(Draw a line segment 3 cm longer than the name line segment. What is the length?)

1. Jeremy ordered five books. Each book cost $3.00. The total cost of shipping and handling was $2.00. How much did Jeremy spend?

   Number sentence _____

   Answer _____

2. Write the names of the months with 31 days. _____

   _____

   What fractional part of the months is this? _____

3. Write each product.

$$\begin{array}{cccccccc} 8 & 9 & 8 & 8 & 2 & 8 & 8 & 3 \\ \times\, 4 & \times\, 8 & \times\, 7 & \times\, 5 & \times\, 8 & \times\, 8 & \times\, 6 & \times\, 8 \end{array}$$

4. How many cups of water will you need to fill these half gallon containers?

   _____ cups

5. Kyle told the class that the minute hand on the clock looks like a horizontal line segment.

   Write the two possible digital times.

6. Shade the thermometer to show 57°F. Will water freeze? _____

7. Use the correct comparison symbol (>, <, or =).

   $73 - 42$ ☐ 6×5 $\sqrt{36}$ ☐ $14 - 9$

   $20 \div 10$ ☐ $\sqrt{4}$ $5 \times 9 - 2$ ☐ $3 \times 7 + 20$

100°F
90°F
80°F
70°F
60°F
50°F
40°F
30°F
20°F
10°F
0°F
−10°F
−20°F

3-85Wa

1. Letha ordered four records. The cost of each record was $10.00. The total cost of shipping and handling was $3.00. How much did Letha spend?

   Number sentence _____ Answer _____

2. Write the names of the months with exactly 30 days. _____

   _____

   What fractional part of the months is this? _____

3. Fill in the missing factors.

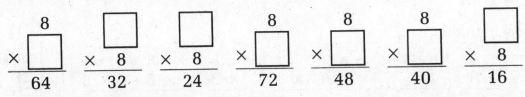

4. How many cups of water will you need to fill these half gallon containers?

 _____ cups

5. Margaret told the class that the minute hand on the clock looks like a vertical line segment.

   9: [____]   9: [____]

   Write the two possible digital times.

6. Shade the thermometer to show 27°F. Will water freeze? _____

7. Use the correct comparison symbol (>, <, or =).

   59 − 37 [ ] 4 × 6   √81 [ ] 17 − 9

   800 ÷ 10 [ ] 16 + 74   4 × 3 + 2 [ ] 2 × 8 − 3

100°F
90°F
80°F
70°F
60°F
50°F
40°F
30°F
20°F
10°F
0°F
−10°F
−20°F

Name _____

M 16.0

```
   5        8        8        2        4
 × 8      × 1      × 7      × 8      × 8
```

```
   8        8        8        3        9
 × 8      × 0      × 6      × 8      × 8
```

```
   1        8        5        8        3
 × 8      × 8      × 8      × 2      × 8
```

```
   8        8        0        6        8
 × 4      × 9      × 8      × 8      × 7
```

```
   8        2        9        4        8
 × 3      × 8      × 8      × 8      × 6
```

Score: _____

3-86Fa

Name •

(Draw a 120 mm line segment.)

Date •

(Draw a $3\frac{1}{2}''$ line segment.)

1. The first part of the fifty-minute hike took fifteen minutes. How long will the last part take?

Number sentence _____ Answer _____

2. Make a tally and a graph showing the number of words in Problem 1 containing from 1 to 8 letters.

letters in each word	number of words

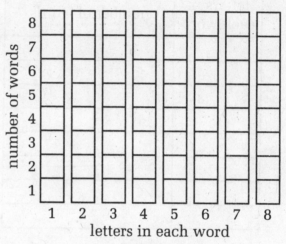

3. Write a number sentence for each of these pictures (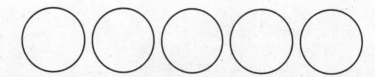 = pencil)

A. 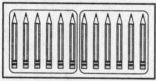   B. 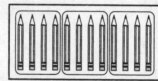   C.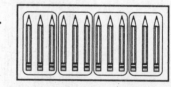

_____   _____   _____

Which picture shows how 4 children will share the pencils? _____

How many pencils will each child have? _____

4. Find the sums.

$$\begin{array}{r} \$6\,6\,4\,.\,3\,4 \\ +\ 2\,5\,3\,.\,7\,1 \\ \hline \end{array} \qquad \begin{array}{r} \$4\,3\,9\,.\,7\,2 \\ +\ 3\,1\,6\,.\,3\,9 \\ \hline \end{array} \qquad \$24.75 + \$39.07$$

5. Shade the circles to show $2\frac{3}{4}$.

How much is not shaded? _____

◯ ◯ ◯ ◯ ◯

Name _____

Date _____

1. The children watched fifteen minutes of a forty-minute movie before lunch. How long will the second part take?

   Number sentence _____ Answer _____

2. Make a tally and a graph showing the number of words in Problem 1 containing from 1 to 8 letters.

letters in each word	number of words

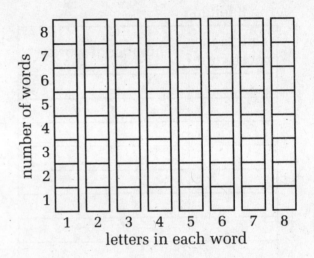

3. Write a number sentence for each of these pictures (▭▭▭▷ = pencil).

   A. 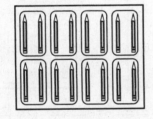   B. 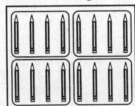   C.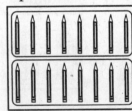

   _____   _____   _____

   Which picture shows how 2 children will share the pencils? _____

   How many pencils will each child have? _____

4. Find the sums.

   $492.35
   + 346.45

   $691.71
   + 139.16

   $49.50 + $37.63

5. Shade the squares to show $3\frac{2}{3}$.

   How much is not shaded? _____

Name _____

Today's Date is _____

Today's Pattern _____
_____

Coin Cup

Q	D	N	P	Total Coins

Today's Problem _____
_____

Today's Date is _____

Today's Pattern _____
_____

Coin Cup

Q	D	N	P.	Total Coins

Today's Problem _____
_____

Today's Date is _____

Today's Pattern _____
_____

Coin Cup

Q	D	N	P	Total Coins

Today's Problem _____
_____

Today's Date is _____

Today's Pattern _____
_____

Coin Cup

Q	D	N	P	Total Coins

Today's Problem _____
_____

Today's Date is _____

Today's Pattern _____
_____

Coin Cup

Q	D	N	P	Total Coins

Today's Problem _____
_____

8	9	14	8	14
− 5	− 3	− 6	− 3	− 8

9	11	8	9	11
− 6	− 3	− 5	− 3	− 8

8	9	14	9	14
− 3	− 6	− 6	− 3	− 8

11	8	9	11	8
− 8	− 5	− 6	− 3	− 3

11	14	8	11	14
− 3	− 8	− 3	− 8	− 6

Score: _____

11	12	12	13	11
− 4	− 5	− 8	− 5	− 7

13	12	12	11	12
− 8	− 4	− 7	− 4	− 8

11	12	12	11	13
− 7	− 5	− 4	− 7	− 8

11	12	13	11	12
− 4	− 8	− 5	− 7	− 4

13	12	12	13	11
− 8	− 7	− 8	− 5	− 7

Score: _____

Name

• (Draw an 85 mm line segment.)

Date •

(Draw a 9 cm line segment.)

1. On March 26th, Miss Gagliardi told the class that they were going on a field trip on June 1st. How many days are there until the field trip?

   Number sentence _____ Answer _____

2. Show four ways to make 50¢.

Q	D	N	P	Total Coins

3. What fractional part of this word is vowels? _____

   What fractional part of this word is consonants? _____

CANADA

4. Someone found the sum of $472.53 and $37.91 like this.

correct answer

   $472.53   Why is this not correct? _____
   +37.91   _____
   $851.63   _____

   Complete the number patterns. Find the rules.

5. 120, 140, 160, _____ , _____ , _____ , _____ , _____ , _____   Rule: _____

6. _____ , _____ , _____ , _____ , _____ , _____ , 40, 44, 48   Rule: _____

7. Use a scrap piece of paper.
   Follow these directions to draw a shape.
   (1) Draw a 5" horizontal line segment near the bottom edge of the paper.
   (2) Draw 2" vertical line segments up from each endpoint.
   (3) Connect the top endpoints of the vertical line segments.

   What shape did you make? _____   What is the perimeter? _____

Name _____

Date _____

1. Debra's birthday is on April 1st. How many days are there until her birthday?

   Number sentence _____   Answer _____

2. Show four ways to make 60¢.

Q	D	N	P	Total Coins

3. What fractional part of this word is vowels? _____

   What fractional part of this word is consonants? _____

   MEXICO

4. Someone found the sum of $184.58 and $265.91 like this.

correct answer

   $184.58   Why is this not correct? _____
   + 265.91   _____
   $440.49   _____

   Complete the number patterns. Find the rules.

5. _____ , _____ , _____ , 320, 300, 280, _____ , _____ , _____   Rule: _____

6. 179, 177, 175, _____ , _____ , _____ , _____ , _____ , _____   Rule: _____

7. Today's number is _____. Write four number sentences. Use addition, subtraction, multiplication, and division.

   _____   _____

   _____   _____

40°C	40°C	40°C	40°C
30°C	30°C	30°C	30°C
20°C	20°C	20°C	20°C
10°C	10°C	10°C	10°C
0°C	0°C	0°C	0°C
−10°C	−10°C	−10°C	−10°C
−20°C	−20°C	−20°C	−20°C
−30°C	−30°C	−30°C	−30°C

Name _____

8 − 5	9 − 3	14 − 6	8 − 3	14 − 8
9 − 6	11 − 3	8 − 5	9 − 3	11 − 8
8 − 3	9 − 6	14 − 6	9 − 3	14 − 8
11 − 8	8 − 5	9 − 6	11 − 3	8 − 3
11 − 3	14 − 8	8 − 3	11 − 8	14 − 6

Score: _____

Name _____ •

(Draw a 9 cm 3 mm line segment.)

Date _____

•

(Draw a $1\frac{1}{2}$" line segment.)

1. Use the chart to answer the question. Curtis wants to buy two markers and four erasers. How much money will he need?

Number sentence _____

Answer _____

	Single	Package of 2	Package of 4
Pencils	15¢	25¢	40¢
Markers	30¢	50¢	85¢
Erasers	10¢	15¢	25¢

2. What temperature is shown on thermometer A? _____

3. Shade thermometer B to show 29°C.

4. What are the smudged digits?

$$63 + \text{\textbf{\textit{8}}}8 = 81 \qquad 490 + 20\text{\textbf{\textit{8}}} = 693$$

_____ _____

$$5\text{\textbf{\textit{8}}}0 - 210 = 370$$

_____

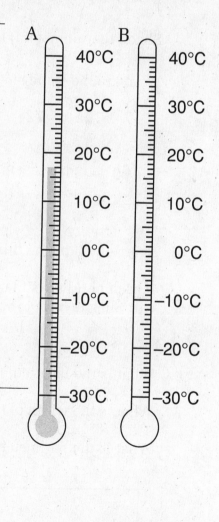

5. Carol will be the fifth child to see the doctor.

How many children are before her? _____

If each child's visit takes 10 minutes, how long will Carol have to wait to see the doctor? _____

6. What is the length of the rectangle? _____ cm

What is the width of the rectangle? _____ cm

What is the perimeter of the rectangle? _____ cm

7. Divide the rectangle in Problem 6 into fourths. Shade three parts.
What fractional part is shaded? _____

What fractional part is not shaded? _____

Name _____

Date _____

1. Use the chart to answer the question. Judy wants to buy two pencils and two markers. How much money will she need?

	Single	Package of 2	Package of 4
Pencils	15¢	25¢	40¢
Markers	30¢	50¢	85¢
Erasers	10¢	15¢	25¢

Number sentence _____

Answer _____

2. What temperature is shown on thermometer A? _____

3. Shade thermometer B to show 14°C.

4. What are the smudged digits?

   47 + ❙5 = 72   620 + 20❙ = 825
   ___   ___

   4❙0 − 310 = 180
   ___

5. Sherrie will be the third child to see the dentist.

   If each child's visit takes 20 minutes, how long will Sherrie have to wait to see the dentist? _____

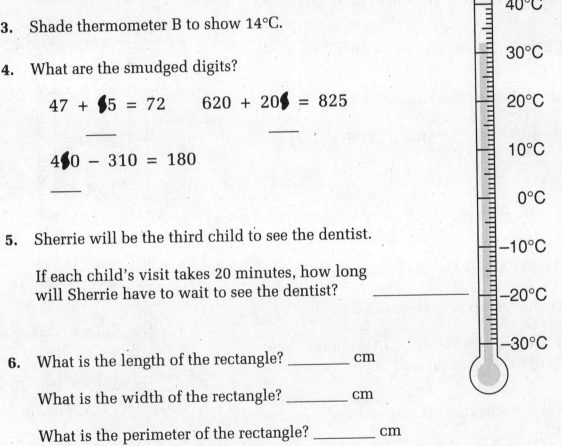

6. What is the length of the rectangle? _____ cm

   What is the width of the rectangle? _____ cm

   What is the perimeter of the rectangle? _____ cm

   10 cm

   1 cm

7. Divide the rectangle in Problem 6 into thirds.
   Shade one part.
   What fractional part is shaded? _____

   What fractional part is not shaded? _____

Name _____

$\frac{1}{2}$ of 12 = _____ $\frac{1}{3}$ of 12 = _____

$\frac{1}{4}$ of 12 = _____ $\frac{1}{6}$ of 12 = _____

Find these answers using the pennies.

$\frac{1}{2}$ of 10 = _____ $\frac{1}{3}$ of 9 = _____ $\frac{1}{2}$ of 6 = _____

$\frac{1}{3}$ of 6 = _____ $\frac{1}{4}$ of 4 = _____ $\frac{1}{3}$ of 3 = _____

$\frac{1}{4}$ of 8 = _____ $\frac{1}{2}$ of 8 = _____ $\frac{1}{2}$ of 2 = _____

5 × 8	8 × 1	8 × 7	2 × 8	4 × 8
8 × 8	8 × 0	8 × 6	3 × 8	9 × 8
1 × 8	8 × 8	5 × 8	8 × 2	3 × 8
8 × 4	8 × 9	0 × 8	6 × 8	8 × 7
8 × 3	2 × 8	9 × 8	4 × 8	8 × 6

Score: _____

3-89Fa

Name •
(Draw an 85 mm line segment.)

Date •

(Draw a line segment 10 mm longer than your name line segment.)

1. Mrs. Wachter drove Jared, his sister, and three friends to the movies. How many children did Mrs. Wachter drive to the movies?

    Number sentence _____ Answer _____

2. Write $609.17 as you would on a check.

    _____ DOLLARS

    Write four hundred seven using digits. _____

3. These are pizzas.
    Divide the first pizza in half.

    Divide the second pizza into fourths.

    Divide the third pizza into eighths.

    Each pizza will have eight
    pieces of pepperoni (•).

    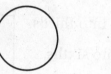

    $\frac{1}{2}$ of 8 = _____ $\frac{1}{4}$ of 8 = _____ $\frac{1}{8}$ of 8 = _____

    Draw the pepperoni on the pizzas so that each piece has the same amount.

4. John's mother was born in 1960. How old is she? _____

5. Find the sums. $718.57 + $84.26 $392.45 + $229.79

    Complete the patterns. Find the rules.

6. 0, $\frac{1}{2}$, 1, 1$\frac{1}{2}$, 2, _____ , _____ , _____ , _____   Rule: _____

7. _____ , _____ , _____ , 195, 190, 185, _____ , _____ , _____   Rule: _____

Name _____

Date _____

1. Karen invited Davelle, Joan, and four other children to her party. How many children were invited to the party?

   Number sentence _____ Answer _____

2. Write $803.12 as you would on a check.

   _____ DOLLARS

   Write seven hundred sixty using digits. _____

3. These are pizzas. Divide the first pizza in half.

   Divide the second pizza into thirds.

   Divide the third pizza into sixths.

   Each pizza will have six pieces of pepperoni (●).

   $\frac{1}{2}$ of 6 = _____ $\frac{1}{3}$ of 6 = _____ $\frac{1}{6}$ of 6 = _____

   Draw the pepperoni on the pizzas so that each piece has the same amount.

4. Tom's father was born in 1950. How old is he? _____

5. Find the sums. $472.38 + $95.84 $756.95 + $145.37

   Complete the patterns. Find the rules.

6. 15, $14\frac{1}{2}$, 14, $13\frac{1}{2}$, _____ , _____ , _____ , _____   Rule: _____

7. _____ , _____ , _____ , _____ , _____ , _____ , 206, 208, 210   Rule: _____

Name •

(Draw a $4\frac{1}{2}$" line segment.)

Date •

(Draw a 73 mm line segment.)

1. Felicia has dance lessons once a week. Each lesson is two hours long. How many hours of dance lessons will Felicia have in 6 weeks?

    Number sentence _____ Answer _____

2. The high temperatures yesterday in Topeka, Jackson, Trenton, and Indianapolis were 31°F, 74°F, 46°F, and 29°F, respectively. Write the names of the cities and their temperatures in order from coldest to warmest.

    _____   _____   _____   _____

    _____°F   _____°F   _____°F   _____°F

    How much warmer was it in Topeka than in Indianapolis? _____

3. Write a check to your teacher for $372.25.

	Date _____
PAY TO THE ORDER OF _____	$ [ ]
_____ DOLLARS	
	_____

4. What is the length of the rectangle? _____ cm

    What is the width of the rectangle? _____ cm

    What is the perimeter of the rectangle? _____ cm

5. Divide the rectangle in Problem 4 into eighths.

    Shade two parts.

    What fractional part is shaded? _____

    What fractional part is not shaded? _____

6. Write a number sentence for each of these pictures. ($\bigcirc$ = cherry)

A. 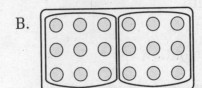   B.   C.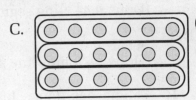

_____   _____   _____

Which picture shows how 3 children will share the cherries? _____

How many cherries will each child have? _____

7. Shade the thermometer to show 73°F.

8. Use the correct comparison symbol (>, <, or =).

$\sqrt{81}$ ☐ $110 \div 10$ $\sqrt{36}$ ☐ $\sqrt{25} + 2$

9. Find the sums.

```
 $2 4 3 . 0 0
+ 3 2 7 . 0 0
```
          $69.00 + $140.00 $572.00 + $389.00

10. Show eight fifty-five on the clocks.

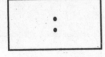

8 − 5	9 − 3	14 − 6	8 − 3	14 − 8
9 − 6	11 − 3	8 − 5	9 − 3	11 − 8
8 − 3	9 − 6	14 − 6	9 − 3	14 − 8
11 − 8	8 − 5	9 − 6	11 − 3	8 − 3
11 − 3	14 − 8	8 − 3	11 − 8	14 − 6

Score: _____

Name _____

Today's Date is _____

Today's Pattern

_____

_____

Today's Problem

Coin Cup

Q	D	N	P	Total Coins
				_____

Today's Date is _____

Today's Pattern

_____

_____

Today's Problem

Coin Cup

Q	D	N	P	Total Coins
				_____

Today's Date is _____

Today's Pattern

_____

_____

Today's Problem

Coin Cup

Q	D	N	P	Total Coins
				_____

Today's Date is _____

Today's Pattern

_____

_____

Today's Problem

Coin Cup

Q	D	N	P	Total Coins
				_____

Today's Date is _____

Today's Pattern

_____

_____

Today's Problem

Coin Cup

Q	D	N	P	Total Coins
				_____

Name _____

11 − 4	12 − 5	12 − 8	13 − 5	11 − 7
13 − 8	12 − 4	12 − 7	11 − 4	12 − 8
11 − 7	12 − 5	12 − 4	11 − 7	13 − 8
11 − 4	12 − 8	13 − 5	11 − 7	12 − 4
13 − 8	12 − 7	12 − 8	13 − 5	11 − 7

Score: _____

Name _____ •

(Draw a 3" line segment.)

Date _____ •

(Draw a congruent line segment. It is _____ mm long.)

1. LeVaughn remembered that the perimeter of the rectangular garden is 32 feet. He also remembered that the width of the garden is 6 feet. He forgot the length. Draw a sketch of the garden to help LeVaughn find the length.

   What is the length? _____

2. Write this amount using digits.

   _____ four hundred two and $\frac{27}{100}$ _____   DOLLARS $ [   ]

3. James, Nicole, Clem, and Crystal will share a dozen cookies. Draw the cookies on the children's plates.

   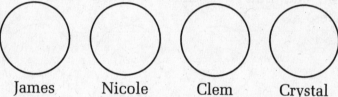

   James   Nicole   Clem   Crystal

   What fractional part of the cookies will each child receive? _____

4. Carisa will be 13 years old on the last day of August five years from now.

   What is the date of her thirteenth birthday? _____

5. Use the correct comparison symbol (> , < , or =).

   $430 - 300$ [ ] $73 + 57$ $\sqrt{64} - 4$ [ ] $\sqrt{36}$

   4×9 [ ] $220 \div 10$ $4 \times 9 + 10$ [ ] 3 tens and 14 ones

   6×8 [ ] 7×7 cups in 1 quart [ ] millimeters in 1 centimeter

6. Find the sums.

   $298.50 + $67.95 + $315.92 = _____

   ```
   $1 2 1.6 5          $6 2 8.4 9
     3 4 7.6 7            6 2.1 8
   + 4 1 2.9 3         + 1 8 4.5 3
   ```

Name _____

Date _____

1. Karen remembered that the perimeter of the picture is 64 inches. She knows that the width is 12 inches. Draw a sketch to help Karen find the length of the picture.

    What is the length? _____

2. Write this amount using digits.

    three hundred sixty and $\frac{12}{100}$ DOLLARS $
    _____

3. Rodney, Jason, and Luis will share a dozen cookies. Draw the cookies on the children's plates.

    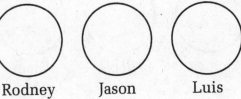

          Rodney   Jason   Luis

    What fractional part of the cookies will each child receive? _____

4. Rajan will be 13 years old on the last day of September four years from now.

    What is the date of his thirteenth birthday? _____

5. Use the correct comparison symbol (>, <, or =).

    $550 - 400$ ☐ $84 + 76$ $\sqrt{81} - 2$ ☐ $\sqrt{49}$

    4×3 ☐ $130 \div 10$ 5 tens and 12 ones ☐ $8 \times 7 + 10$

    8×3 ☐ 4×6 cups in 1 half gallon ☐ inches in 1 foot

6. Find the sums.

    $335.19 + \$47.16 + \$342.65 = $ _____

    $\begin{array}{r} \$2\,9\,1.4\,8 \\ 1\,2\,4.5\,8 \\ + \,4\,8\,2.2\,8 \\ \hline \end{array}$ $\begin{array}{r} \$5\,5\,2.9\,0 \\ 2\,8\,3.7\,4 \\ + \;\;1\,3.9\,3 \\ \hline \end{array}$

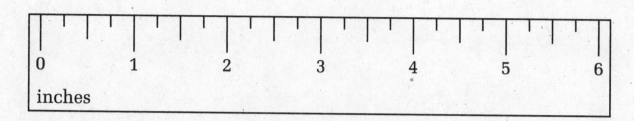

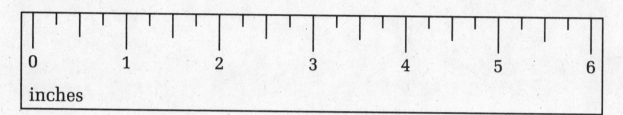

Measure these line segments.

1. •————————————• _____ "

2. •————————————• _____ "

3. •————• _____ "

4. •————————• _____ "

5. •——————————• _____ "

6. •——————• _____ "

7. •———• _____ "

inches
0 1 2 3 4 5 6

5 + 4	4 + 6	2 + 3	6 + 8	5 + 0	0 + 9	4 + 8	5 + 6	1 + 3	6 + 1
2 + 5	0 + 8	6 + 7	0 + 3	2 + 9	8 + 8	6 + 0	1 + 9	6 + 9	8 + 4
1 + 6	9 + 8	1 + 5	4 + 9	8 + 6	2 + 4	7 + 9	8 + 3	4 + 3	0 + 4
7 + 3	3 + 2	7 + 0	7 + 2	1 + 4	6 + 5	3 + 6	3 + 0	8 + 0	9 + 7
9 + 9	7 + 8	7 + 4	9 + 5	5 + 7	1 + 8	0 + 1	8 + 9	2 + 7	7 + 5
0 + 7	6 + 6	3 + 3	2 + 6	6 + 2	9 + 2	5 + 8	4 + 5	9 + 3	3 + 1
5 + 1	4 + 1	8 + 1	3 + 4	0 + 0	4 + 4	9 + 6	1 + 2	5 + 9	2 + 8
6 + 4	8 + 7	0 + 6	7 + 6	1 + 7	3 + 7	9 + 0	4 + 7	0 + 2	5 + 3
2 + 2	2 + 0	3 + 9	5 + 5	3 + 5	0 + 5	7 + 7	2 + 6	3 + 8	4 + 0
9 + 1	9 + 4	5 + 2	1 + 0	8 + 2	6 + 3	4 + 2	7 + 1	1 + 1	8 + 5

3-92Fa

Name •_____•
(Measure this line segment. _____")

Date •
(Draw a $4\frac{1}{4}$" line segment.)

1. How many days are there in the last three months of the year?

   Number sentence _____ Answer _____

2. Use the line graph to answer these questions.

   On what day was the
   temperature the highest? _____

   About what was the
   temperature on February 23rd? _____

   On what date was the
   temperature above freezing? _____

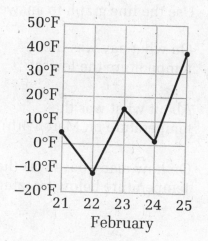

50°F
40°F
30°F
20°F
10°F
0°F
−10°F
−20°F
21 22 23 24 25
February

3. What fractional part of the beads is white? _____

4. Mrs. Liberti was born in 1961. How old will she be on her birthday this year? _____

5. Circle the temperatures whose rounded value is 50°.

   43°   57°   55°   45°   53°   48°   59°

6. Find the answers.

   $48 \times 10 =$ _____

   $260 \div 10 =$ _____

   $37 + 49 =$ _____

   $\sqrt{49} - \sqrt{36} =$ _____

   $250 - 40 =$ _____

   $65 + 21 =$ _____

$$
\begin{array}{r}
\$2\,8.0\,3 \\
5\,1\,8.5\,6 \\
+\ 2\,5\,8.4\,8 \\
\hline
\end{array}
$$

7. I have 7 ten-dollar bills and 15 one-dollar bills. How much money do I have? _____

Name _____   **LESSON 92B**
                                                   Math 3
Date _____

1. What is the total number of days in the months of June, July, and August?

    Number sentence _____ Answer _____

2. Use the line graph to answer these questions.

    On what day was the
    temperature the lowest? _____

    About what was the
    temperature on March 4th? _____

    On how many days was the
    temperature below freezing? _____

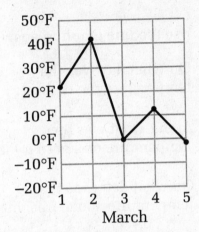

3. What fractional part of the beads is black? _____

4. Courtney was born in 1975. How old will she be on her birthday this year? _____

5. Circle the temperatures whose rounded value is 70°.

    72°   65°   77°   62°   69°   70°   75°   73°

6. Find the answers.

    $10 \times 35 =$ _____ $\sqrt{81} - \sqrt{16} =$ _____ $6 1 9.3 0
                                                               9 2.3 8
    $490 \div 10 =$ _____ $140 - 30 =$ _____   + 1 7 8.2 8
                                                               _____

    $26 + 57 =$ _____ $39 + 41 =$ _____

7. I have 12 one-dollar bills and 6 ten-dollar bills. How much money do I have? _____

11	12	12	13	11
− 4	− 5	− 8	− 5	− 7

13	12	12	11	12
− 8	− 4	− 7	− 4	− 8

11	12	12	11	13
− 7	− 5	− 4	− 7	− 8

11	12	13	11	12
− 4	− 8	− 5	− 7	− 4

13	12	12	13	11
− 8	− 7	− 8	− 5	− 7

Score: _____

3-93Fa

$$
\begin{array}{r} 4 \\ \times\ 8 \\ \hline \end{array}
\qquad
\begin{array}{r} 5 \\ \times\ 9 \\ \hline \end{array}
\qquad
\begin{array}{r} 8 \\ \times\ 2 \\ \hline \end{array}
\qquad
\begin{array}{r} 5 \\ \times\ 4 \\ \hline \end{array}
\qquad
\begin{array}{r} 7 \\ \times\ 8 \\ \hline \end{array}
$$

$$
\begin{array}{r} 5 \\ \times\ 5 \\ \hline \end{array}
\qquad
\begin{array}{r} 8 \\ \times\ 3 \\ \hline \end{array}
\qquad
\begin{array}{r} 7 \\ \times\ 4 \\ \hline \end{array}
\qquad
\begin{array}{r} 9 \\ \times\ 8 \\ \hline \end{array}
\qquad
\begin{array}{r} 6 \\ \times\ 2 \\ \hline \end{array}
$$

$$
\begin{array}{r} 5 \\ \times\ 8 \\ \hline \end{array}
\qquad
\begin{array}{r} 3 \\ \times\ 7 \\ \hline \end{array}
\qquad
\begin{array}{r} 8 \\ \times\ 6 \\ \hline \end{array}
\qquad
\begin{array}{r} 6 \\ \times\ 4 \\ \hline \end{array}
\qquad
\begin{array}{r} 8 \\ \times\ 8 \\ \hline \end{array}
$$

$$
\begin{array}{r} 6 \\ \times\ 7 \\ \hline \end{array}
\qquad
\begin{array}{r} 1 \\ \times\ 8 \\ \hline \end{array}
\qquad
\begin{array}{r} 4 \\ \times\ 9 \\ \hline \end{array}
\qquad
\begin{array}{r} 8 \\ \times\ 10 \\ \hline \end{array}
\qquad
\begin{array}{r} 1 \\ \times\ 1 \\ \hline \end{array}
$$

$$
\begin{array}{r} 0 \\ \times\ 8 \\ \hline \end{array}
\qquad
\begin{array}{r} 3 \\ \times\ 4 \\ \hline \end{array}
\qquad
\begin{array}{r} 8 \\ \times\ 6 \\ \hline \end{array}
\qquad
\begin{array}{r} 7 \\ \times\ 7 \\ \hline \end{array}
\qquad
\begin{array}{r} 8 \\ \times\ 9 \\ \hline \end{array}
$$

Score: _____

Name _____

(Measure this line segment. _____")

Date •

(Draw a $4\frac{1}{4}$" line segment.)

1. A pie has 8 equal pieces. Bob ate $\frac{3}{8}$ of the pie, Linda ate $\frac{1}{8}$ of the pie, and Marlynn ate $\frac{2}{8}$ of the pie. Divide the pie into 8 equal pieces.

   Write the first initial of each child's name in the pieces they ate.

   What fractional part of the pie is left for John? _____

2. I have 3 one-dollar bills and 4 hundred-dollar bills.

   How much money do I have? _____

3. Peter was born in 1931, Nils was born in 1965, and Anna was born in 1952. How old will each person be on this year's birthday?

   Peter _____   Nils _____   Anna _____

   Circle the name of the youngest person.

4. Use the pictograph to answer these questions.

   How many lunch boxes does ☐ equal? _____

   How many pink lunch boxes are there? _____

   How many more yellow lunch boxes are there than blue lunch boxes? _____

   How many lunch boxes are shown on this graph altogether? _____

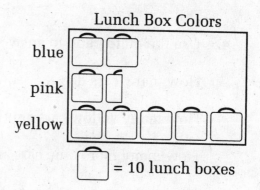

Lunch Box Colors

blue

pink

yellow

☐ = 10 lunch boxes

5. It's twenty-eight minutes past four in the morning. Show the time on the clock face and write the digital time. _____

6. Find the sums.

   $297.35 + $624.28 $73.51 + $346.95

Name _____

Date _____

1. A cake has 6 equal pieces. Ken ate $\frac{1}{6}$ of the cake, Tania ate $\frac{3}{6}$ of the cake, and Carly ate $\frac{1}{6}$ of the cake. Divide the cake into 6 equal pieces.

   Write the first initial of each child's name on the pieces they ate.

   What fractional part of the cake is left for Sean? _____

2. I have 5 ten-dollar bills and 7 hundred-dollar bills.

   How much money do I have? _____

3. Shannon was born in 1962, Anthony was born in 1953, and Ellen was born in 1946. How old will each person be on this year's birthday?

   Shannon _____   Anthony _____   Ellen _____

   Circle the name of the youngest person.

4. Use the pictograph to answer these questions.   CAR COLORS

   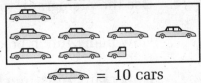

   How many cars does 🚗 equal? _____

   How many yellow cars are there? _____

   How many more blue cars are there than red cars? _____

   How many cars are shown on this graph altogether? _____

5. It's thirty-seven minutes past three in the afternoon. Show the time on the clock face and write the digital time. _____

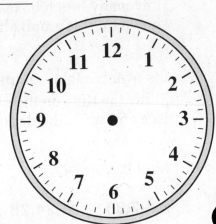

6. Find the sums.

   $427.47 + $382.65 $293.17 + $58.34

$$\begin{array}{r} 4 \\ \times\ 8 \\ \hline \end{array} \qquad \begin{array}{r} 5 \\ \times\ 9 \\ \hline \end{array} \qquad \begin{array}{r} 8 \\ \times\ 2 \\ \hline \end{array} \qquad \begin{array}{r} 5 \\ \times\ 4 \\ \hline \end{array} \qquad \begin{array}{r} 7 \\ \times\ 8 \\ \hline \end{array}$$

$$\begin{array}{r} 5 \\ \times\ 5 \\ \hline \end{array} \qquad \begin{array}{r} 8 \\ \times\ 3 \\ \hline \end{array} \qquad \begin{array}{r} 7 \\ \times\ 4 \\ \hline \end{array} \qquad \begin{array}{r} 9 \\ \times\ 8 \\ \hline \end{array} \qquad \begin{array}{r} 6 \\ \times\ 2 \\ \hline \end{array}$$

$$\begin{array}{r} 5 \\ \times\ 8 \\ \hline \end{array} \qquad \begin{array}{r} 3 \\ \times\ 7 \\ \hline \end{array} \qquad \begin{array}{r} 8 \\ \times\ 6 \\ \hline \end{array} \qquad \begin{array}{r} 6 \\ \times\ 4 \\ \hline \end{array} \qquad \begin{array}{r} 8 \\ \times\ 8 \\ \hline \end{array}$$

$$\begin{array}{r} 6 \\ \times\ 7 \\ \hline \end{array} \qquad \begin{array}{r} 1 \\ \times\ 8 \\ \hline \end{array} \qquad \begin{array}{r} 4 \\ \times\ 9 \\ \hline \end{array} \qquad \begin{array}{r} 8 \\ \times\ 10 \\ \hline \end{array} \qquad \begin{array}{r} 1 \\ \times\ 1 \\ \hline \end{array}$$

$$\begin{array}{r} 0 \\ \times\ 8 \\ \hline \end{array} \qquad \begin{array}{r} 3 \\ \times\ 4 \\ \hline \end{array} \qquad \begin{array}{r} 8 \\ \times\ 6 \\ \hline \end{array} \qquad \begin{array}{r} 7 \\ \times\ 7 \\ \hline \end{array} \qquad \begin{array}{r} 8 \\ \times\ 9 \\ \hline \end{array}$$

Score: _____

Name _____

(Draw a $4\frac{1}{4}"$ line segment.)

Date _____

●——————————————●

(Measure this line segment. _____ cm _____ mm)

1. I'm thinking of a number between 60 and 65. The sum of the digits is 9.

   What is my number? _____

2. Draw candies (•) to find each answer.

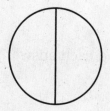 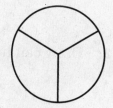

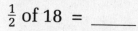 $\frac{1}{2}$ of 18 = _____ $\frac{1}{3}$ of 15 = _____

3. Show 4 ways to make 63¢.

Q	D	N	P	Total Coins

4. It's seven minutes past five in the afternoon.

   Write the time using digits. _____
   Show the time on the clock.
   What time will it be two hours later? _____

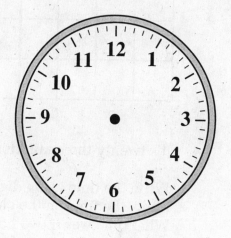

5. Fill in the missing compass directions.

6. Find the answers.

$$\begin{array}{r} 6\ 7 \\ -\ 4\ 8 \\ \hline \end{array} \qquad \begin{array}{r} 8\ 2 \\ -\ 4\ 9 \\ \hline \end{array} \qquad \begin{array}{r} 5\ 8 \\ -\ 3\ 4 \\ \hline \end{array}$$

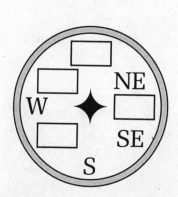

Name _____

Date _____

1. I'm thinking of a number between 24 and 29. The sum of the digits is 8.

   What is my number? _____

2. Draw candies (•) to find each answer.

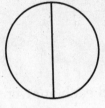

   $\frac{1}{2}$ of 14 = _____ $\frac{1}{4}$ of 20 = _____

3. Show 4 ways to make 78¢.

Q	D	N	P	Total Coins

4. It's twenty-three minutes past six in the morning.

   Write the time using digits. _____
   Show the time on the clock.
   What time was it two hours ago? _____

5. Fill in the missing compass directions.

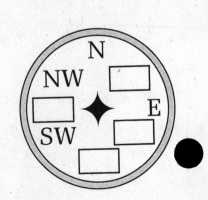

6. Find the answers.

   73   89   36
 − 55   − 36   − 17
 _____ _____ _____

Name

Today's Date is

Today's Pattern

Coin Cup

Q	D	N	P	Total Coins

Today's Problem

Today's Date is

Today's Pattern

Coin Cup

Q	D	N	P	Total Coins

Today's Problem

Today's Date is

Today's Pattern

Coin Cup

Q	D	N	P	Total Coins

Today's Problem

Today's Date is

Today's Pattern

Coin Cup

Q	D	N	P	Total Coins

Today's Problem

Today's Date is

Today's Pattern

Coin Cup

Q	D	N	P	Total Coins

Today's Problem

3-°R1Ma

Name •—————————————————•

Date •

(Draw a congruent line segment.)

1. Gail had some money. Her sister gave her 45¢. Now she has 79¢. How much money did Gail have originally?

   Number sentence _____ Answer _____

2. If today is April 29th, how many more days will there be until the fourth of July?

   Number sentence _____ Answer _____

3. Draw a line graph to show the following temperatures.

Date	Temperature
Feb. 1	45°F
Feb. 2	30°F
Feb. 3	−5°F
Feb. 4	25°F
Feb. 5	12°F

   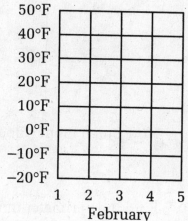

   On what date was the temperature the lowest? _____

   How many days had a
   temperature below freezing? _____

4. It is morning. Mrs. Barslow tells the children that the guest reader will visit the class three hours from now. The clock shows the time now.

   At what time will the guest reader arrive? _____

5. Write November 9, 1948 using digits. _____

   Write 1/3/50 using words. _____

3-95Aa

6. Write these numbers using words.

207 _____

943 _____

690 _____

7. Tim has 3 quarters, 2 dimes, 2 nickels, and 4 pennies.
Draw the coins.

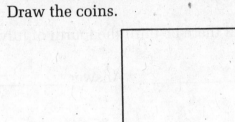

How much money does he have? _____

8. Find the perimeter in centimeters of the rectangle in Problem 7. _____ cm

9. Find the answers.

   $216.00 + $390.00 $263.00 + $28.00 $562.00 + $157.00

10. Marilyn's family ate $2\frac{1}{4}$ pies.

Color the pies to show
how much pie they ate.

How much pie is left? _____

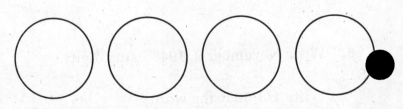

2	7	1	3	4
× 3	× 3	× 3	× 5	× 3

6	3	3	9	3
× 3	× 8	× 4	× 3	× 3

3	8	3	9	3
× 0	× 3	× 5	× 3	× 6

8	3	3	6	0
× 3	× 2	× 4	× 3	× 3

3	1	6	3	3
× 7	× 3	× 3	× 7	× 3

Score: _____

3-95Fa

Name _____

(Draw a $4\frac{3}{4}$" line segment.)

Date _____

(Draw a congruent line segment. It is about _____ cm long.)

1. Erica bought five pencils for 30¢ each and two books for $1.00 each. How much money did she spend?

   Number sentence _____ Answer _____

2. It's morning.
   What time is it? _____

   What time will it be
   two hours from now? _____

3. Fill in the missing numbers.

   [ ] × 3 = 27   3 × 8 = [ ]   6 × 3 = [ ]   6 × [ ] = 48

   6 × 6 = [ ]   6 × 9 = [ ]   3 × [ ] = 12   [ ] × 6 = 24

4. The ✿ are frosting roses on a cake.
   How many roses are on the cake? _____
   Show how to cut the cake into equal size
   pieces so that each piece has two roses.

   How many pieces did you make? _____

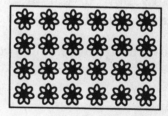

5. Find each answer.

   $$\begin{array}{r} 93 \\ -\ 25 \\ \hline \end{array} \qquad \begin{array}{r} 48 \\ -\ 34 \\ \hline \end{array} \qquad \begin{array}{r} 63 \\ -\ 19 \\ \hline \end{array} \qquad \begin{array}{r} \$217.39 \\ 384.57 \\ +\ 103.54 \\ \hline \end{array}$$

6. What are the smudged digits?

   $4 + 4 + 4 + 4 + 4 = $ ❢ $\times 4$ $29 + 51 = $ ❢ $\times 10$ $\sqrt{64} = 10 - $ ❢

   _____   _____   _____

Name _____

Date _____

1. Jessica bought seven pens for 60¢ each and three books for $1.00 each. How much money did she spend?

   Number sentence _____ Answer _____

2. It's afternoon.
   What time is it? _____

   What time will it be
   three hours from now? _____

3. Fill in the missing numbers.

   $\boxed{} \times 3 = 9$ $3 \times 6 = \boxed{}$ $3 \times 9 = \boxed{}$ $6 \times \boxed{} = 54$

   $6 \times 4 = \boxed{}$ $6 \times 8 = \boxed{}$ $3 \times \boxed{} = 18$ $\boxed{} \times 6 = 42$

4. The ❀ are frosting roses on a cake.
   How many roses are on the cake? _____
   Show how to cut the cake into equal size
   pieces so that each piece has two roses.

   How many pieces did you make? _____

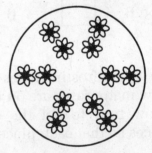

5. Find each answer.

   $$\begin{array}{r} 8\,2 \\ -\,4\,4 \\ \hline \end{array} \qquad \begin{array}{r} 2\,6 \\ -\,1\,3 \\ \hline \end{array} \qquad \begin{array}{r} 5\,4 \\ -\,3\,1 \\ \hline \end{array} \qquad \begin{array}{r} \$4\,2.6\,7 \\ 3\,1\,8.2\,3 \\ +\,4\,1\,7.2\,5 \\ \hline \end{array}$$

6. What are the smudged digits?

   $6 + 6 + 6 + 6 = \text{❚} \times 6$ $27 + 33 = \text{❚} \times 10$ $\sqrt{49} = 8 - \text{❚}$

   _____   _____   _____

2	7	1	3	4
× 3	× 3	× 3	× 5	× 3

6	3	3	9	3
× 3	× 8	× 4	× 3	× 3

3	8	3	9	3
× 0	× 3	× 5	× 3	× 6

8	3	3	6	0
× 3	× 2	× 4	× 3	× 3

3	1	6	3	3
× 7	× 3	× 3	× 7	× 3

Score: _____

3-96Fa

Name _____ •   **LESSON 96A**
          (Draw a $3\frac{1}{4}$" line segment.)   *Math 3*

Date •——————————————————————————————•

          (Measure this line segment. _____")

1. Use the map to answer the
    question. How many miles is it
    from West Haven to New London?

    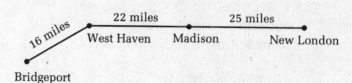

    Number sentence _____ Answer _____

2. Write seven hundred twenty using digits. _____

3. What are the smudged digits?

        21 + 1❚ = 5 × 7   ❚ × 7 = 350 ÷ 10

            ___   ___

4. Ronald has 90¢ to spend. Find three different
    combinations of things he can buy. How much will he
    spend for each combination?

    _____ _____
                                                              | apple | 29¢ |
    _____ _____ | orange | 54¢ |
                                                              | banana | 33¢ |
    _____ _____ | peach | 47¢ |

5. Show eleven thirty-seven on the clock.

    It's morning.

    Write the digital time. _____

    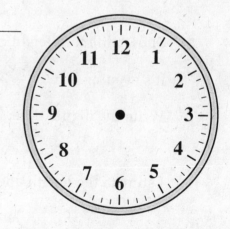

6. Estimate the length and width of your desk.

                    length: _____ feet   width: _____ feet

    How many feet are in one yard? _____

7. Find the answers.   46 − 28   71 − 34   32 − 8

Name _____

Date _____

1. Use the map to answer the question. How many miles is it from Madison to Bridgeport?

   22 miles   25 miles

   16 miles   West Haven   Madison   New London

   Bridgeport

   Number sentence _____ Answer _____

2. Write three hundred seven using digits. _____

3. What are the smudged digits?

   $$2\blacklozenge + 13 = 7 \times 6 \qquad\qquad 250 \div 10 = \blacklozenge \times 5$$

   _____   _____

4. Ashley has 80¢ to spend. Find three different combinations of things she can buy. How much will she spend for each combination?

pen	24¢
pencil	16¢
marker	37¢
pad	45¢

   _____ _____

   _____ _____

   _____ _____

5. Show nine forty-eight on the clock.

   It's evening.

   Write the digital time. _____

6. Estimate the length and width of your bedroom using your feet.

   length: _____ feet   width: _____ feet

   Estimate the distance in yards from your bed to your front door. Pace the distance.

   _____ yards

7. Find the answers.   63 − 45   56 − 19   43 − 7

1.

	100's	10's	1's
$			
−			
$			

2.

	100's	10's	1's
$			
−			
$			

3.

	100's	10's	1's
$			
−			
$			

4.

$			
−			
$			

5.

$			
−			
$			

6.

$			
−			
$			

7.

$			
−			
$			

8.

$			
−			
$			

9.

$			
−			
$			

10.

$			
−			
$			

11.

$			
−			
$			

12.

$			
−			
$			

```
    5        2        6        6        1
  × 6      × 6      × 7      × 3      × 6
  ———      ———      ———      ———      ———


    6        7        0        9        6
  × 4      × 6      × 6      × 6      × 2
  ———      ———      ———      ———      ———


    3        8        6        0        6
  × 6      × 6      × 6      × 6      × 5
  ———      ———      ———      ———      ———


    4        6        7        6        8
  × 6      × 1      × 6      × 3      × 6
  ———      ———      ———      ———      ———


    6        9        6        2        6
  × 5      × 6      × 6      × 6      × 4
  ———      ———      ———      ———      ———
```

Score: _____

3-97Fa

2 × 3	7 × 6	4 × 6	5 × 3	6 × 6
6 × 3	3 × 3	5 × 6	8 × 6	2 × 3
6 × 6	9 × 3	2 × 6	7 × 3	1 × 6
8 × 3	0 × 3	9 × 6	3 × 6	4 × 3
1 × 3	6 × 6	0 × 6	8 × 6	9 × 3

Score: _____

3-97Fb

Name _____•

(Measure this line segment using inches. _____")

Date •

(Draw a $\frac{3}{4}$" line segment.)

1. Gary bought two puzzles for $3 each and a new box of crayons for $2. How much money did he spend?

   Number sentence _____ Answer _____

2. On the last day of January of this year, Lee Capone bought a blouse for $29.75, a skirt for $35.95, and a sweater for $45.50 at Buttons and Bows.

   How much money did she spend? _____

   She paid for the items with a check. Show how she wrote the check.

   Date _____

   PAY TO THE
   ORDER OF _____ $ [   ]

   _____ DOLLARS

   _____

3. Name the months with exactly 30 days. _____

   _____

4. Your classroom door is about how tall?

   20 feet   7 feet   6 yards   40 inches

5. Show how to find each answer.

   $\frac{1}{2}$ of 8 = _____ $\frac{1}{3}$ of 9 = _____ $\frac{1}{4}$ of 4 = _____

3-97Wa

Name _____   **LESSON 97B**
                                                                  Math 3
Date _____

1. Mrs. Kaplan bought two gallons of milk for $2.00 each and a dozen donuts for $4.00.
    How much money did she spend?

    Number sentence _____   Answer _____

2. On the last day of March of this year, Nancy Smith bought a jacket for $54.50, a skirt
    for $25.50, and a pair of pants for $29.50 from Acme Clothes.

    How much money did she spend? _____

    She paid for the items with a check. Show how she wrote the check.

    +---+
    | |
    | Date _____ |
    | |
    | PAY TO THE |
    | ORDER OF   _____ $[_____] |
    | |
    | _____ DOLLARS |
    | |
    | _____ |
    | |
    +---+

3. Name the months with exactly 31 days. _____

    _____

4. Your bed is about how long?

        12 feet   18 inches   2 feet   6 feet   4 yards

5. Show how to find each answer.

                       [ ]

    $\frac{1}{2}$ of 10 = _____ $\frac{1}{3}$ of 6 = _____ $\frac{1}{4}$ of 12 = _____

Name _____

16 − 9	7 − 2	15 − 6	9 − 5	14 − 9
10 − 4	12 − 9	16 − 7	8 − 6	13 − 4
12 − 3	11 − 6	16 − 8	13 − 9	7 − 6
7 − 4	15 − 9	14 − 5	15 − 8	10 − 6
12 − 6	10 − 3	11 − 9	7 − 1	17 − 9

Score: _____

Name •
(Draw a 4" line segment.)

Date •
(Draw a line segment $\frac{1}{4}$" longer than the name line segment.)

1. What will be the date 2 years and 5 days from July 29, 2009? _____

2. Write 298 using words. _____

3. Wendy is standing at the Ⓧ.

   In what direction should she walk to reach spot A? _____

   In what direction should she walk to reach spot D? _____

   In what direction should she walk to reach spot G? _____

4. Show four fifty-one on the clock.
   It's morning. Write the digital time. _____

   How many minutes is
   it until the next hour? _____

5. Find each difference.

   $340 $247 $436
   – 130   – 109   – 192

6. Use the correct comparison symbol (> , < , or =).

   1269 + 3588 ▢ 48 × 100   7 × 4 – 6 ▢ 3 × 8 – 2

   $\sqrt{49} + \sqrt{4}$ ▢ 80 ÷ 10 + 2

   number of days in May ▢ number of cups in a gallon

   number of quarters in $5.00 ▢ number of donuts in one and a half dozen

7. Complete the number patterns. Write the rules.

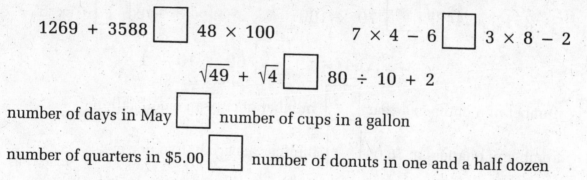

   265, 270, 275, 280, _____ , _____ , _____ , _____ , _____ , _____ Rule: _____

   233, 334, 435, _____ , _____ , _____ , _____ , _____ , _____ Rule: _____

3-98Wa

1. What will be the date 1 year and 4 days from November 29, 2039? _____

2. Write 517 using words. _____

3. Wendy is standing at the ⊗.

   In what direction should she walk to reach spot F? _____

   In what direction should she walk to reach spot C? _____

   In what direction should she walk to reach spot B? _____

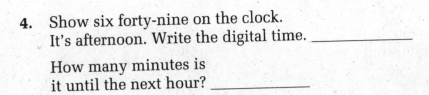 

4. Show six forty-nine on the clock.
   It's afternoon. Write the digital time. _____

   How many minutes is
   it until the next hour? _____

5. Find each difference.

$535	$458	$394
− 317	− 278	− 172

6. Use the correct comparison symbol (> , < , or =).

   2517 + 4482 ☐ 70 × 100   9 × 3 + 8 ☐ 6 × 5 + 6

   $\sqrt{64} - \sqrt{9}$ ☐ 60 ÷ 10 − 1

   number of months in a year ☐ number of cups in a half gallon

   number of quarters in $6.00 ☐ number of eggs in two dozen

7. Complete the number patterns. Write the rules.

   456, 466, 476, 486, _____ , _____ , _____ , _____ , _____ , _____ Rule: _____

   180, 281, 382, _____ , _____ , _____ , _____ , _____ , _____ Rule: _____

Name

Today's Date is _____
Today's Pattern _____
_____

Today's Problem

Coin Cup

Q	D	N	P	Total Coins
				_____

Today's Date is _____
Today's Pattern _____
_____

Today's Problem

Coin Cup

Q	D	N	P	Total Coins
				_____

Today's Date is _____
Today's Pattern _____
_____

Today's Problem

Coin Cup

Q	D	N	P	Total Coins
				_____

Today's Date is _____
Today's Pattern _____
_____

Today's Problem

Coin Cup

Q	D	N	P	Total Coins
				_____

Today's Date is _____
Today's Pattern _____
_____

Today's Problem

Coin Cup

Q	D	N	P	Total Coins
				_____

3-*R1Ma

12	8	9	11	12
− 4	− 3	− 6	− 8	− 5

14	11	13	12	9
− 6	− 4	− 5	− 8	− 3

11	13	12	8	14
− 7	− 8	− 7	− 5	− 8

11	9	12	13	11
− 3	− 6	− 4	− 5	− 8

14	8	11	12	12
− 6	− 3	− 4	− 8	− 5

Score: _____

$$
\begin{array}{r} 5 \\ \times\ 6 \\ \hline \end{array}
\qquad
\begin{array}{r} 2 \\ \times\ 6 \\ \hline \end{array}
\qquad
\begin{array}{r} 6 \\ \times\ 7 \\ \hline \end{array}
\qquad
\begin{array}{r} 6 \\ \times\ 3 \\ \hline \end{array}
\qquad
\begin{array}{r} 1 \\ \times\ 6 \\ \hline \end{array}
$$

$$
\begin{array}{r} 6 \\ \times\ 4 \\ \hline \end{array}
\qquad
\begin{array}{r} 7 \\ \times\ 6 \\ \hline \end{array}
\qquad
\begin{array}{r} 0 \\ \times\ 6 \\ \hline \end{array}
\qquad
\begin{array}{r} 9 \\ \times\ 6 \\ \hline \end{array}
\qquad
\begin{array}{r} 6 \\ \times\ 2 \\ \hline \end{array}
$$

$$
\begin{array}{r} 3 \\ \times\ 6 \\ \hline \end{array}
\qquad
\begin{array}{r} 8 \\ \times\ 6 \\ \hline \end{array}
\qquad
\begin{array}{r} 6 \\ \times\ 6 \\ \hline \end{array}
\qquad
\begin{array}{r} 0 \\ \times\ 6 \\ \hline \end{array}
\qquad
\begin{array}{r} 6 \\ \times\ 5 \\ \hline \end{array}
$$

$$
\begin{array}{r} 4 \\ \times\ 6 \\ \hline \end{array}
\qquad
\begin{array}{r} 6 \\ \times\ 1 \\ \hline \end{array}
\qquad
\begin{array}{r} 7 \\ \times\ 6 \\ \hline \end{array}
\qquad
\begin{array}{r} 6 \\ \times\ 3 \\ \hline \end{array}
\qquad
\begin{array}{r} 8 \\ \times\ 6 \\ \hline \end{array}
$$

$$
\begin{array}{r} 6 \\ \times\ 5 \\ \hline \end{array}
\qquad
\begin{array}{r} 9 \\ \times\ 6 \\ \hline \end{array}
\qquad
\begin{array}{r} 6 \\ \times\ 6 \\ \hline \end{array}
\qquad
\begin{array}{r} 2 \\ \times\ 6 \\ \hline \end{array}
\qquad
\begin{array}{r} 6 \\ \times\ 4 \\ \hline \end{array}
$$

Score: _____

3-99Fb

Name •

(Draw a 113 mm line segment.)

Date •

(Draw a $2\frac{1}{4}''$ line segment.)

1. How much will Mrs. Shapiro pay for two phones and a clock?

   Number sentence _____

   Answer _____

SALE	
Phone	$49.75
Radio	$27.45
Clock	$12.97

2. Write the numbers in expanded form.

   293 _____

   560 _____

3. Write nine hundred sixty-one using digits. _____

4. Draw a picture to show 8 groups of 3 pencils. Circle the number sentence that matches the picture.

   $2 \times 12 = 24$ $\quad$ $8 \times 3 = 24$

   $4 \times 6 = 24$ $\quad$ $8 + 4 + 8 + 4 = 24$

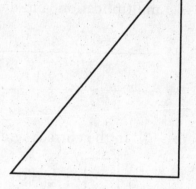

5. Measure each side of the triangle using millimeters.

   oblique line segment _____

   vertical line segment _____

   horizontal line segment _____

   What is the perimeter of the triangle? _____

6. Fill in the correct symbol $(+, -, \times, \text{ or } \div)$.

   $9 \; \boxed{} \; 5 = \sqrt{16}$ $\qquad$ $14 + 58 = 8 \; \boxed{} \; 9$ $\qquad$ $280 \; \boxed{} \; 10 = 7 \times 4$

7. Find the answers.

   $\$239 + \$85$ $\qquad$ $\$647 - \$165$ $\qquad$ $\$21.73 + \$469.74$

Name _____

Date _____

1. How much will Mrs. Morrison pay for two radios and a phone?

SALE	
Phone	$49.75
Radio	$27.45
Clock	$12.97

   Number sentence _____

   Answer _____

2. Write the numbers in expanded form.

   425 _____

   301 _____

3. Write five hundred thirteen using digits. _____

4. Draw a picture to show 6 groups of 8 bananas. Circle the number sentence that matches the picture.

   $4 \times 12 = 48$ $6 \times 8 = 48$

   $40 + 8 = 48$ $12 + 12 + 12 + 12 = 48$

5. Today's number is _____. Write four number sentences. Use addition, subtraction, multiplication, and division.

   _____   _____

   _____   _____

6. Fill in the correct symbol ($+$, $-$, $\times$, or $\div$).

   $6 \ \boxed{} \ 3 = \sqrt{9}$ $48 + 27 = 750 \ \boxed{} \ 10$ $3 \ \boxed{} \ 6 = 2 \times 9$

7. Find the sums.

   $\$356 - \$73$ $\$941 - \$623$ $\$69.74 + \$325.18$

Name •
    (Draw a 98 mm line segment.)

Date •

(Draw a line segment 10 mm longer than the name line segment.)

1. Lauryn bought 5 books. Each book costs $2.00. She also bought a poster for $3.00. How much money did Lauryn spend for the books and the poster?

   Number sentence _____ Answer _____

2. List the months with 31 days. _____

   _____

   _____

3. Sam has 2 quarters, 2 nickels, and 3 pennies. He found 2 dimes, 1 nickel, and 1 penny. Draw the coins.

   _____

   How much money does he have now? _____

4. What temperature is shown on this thermometer? _____

   What is the Celsius temperature at which water boils? _____°C

   What is the Celsius temperature at which water freezes? _____°C

5. Write these numbers using digits.

   four hundred seventy-nine _____

   one hundred thirty _____

   five hundred eight _____

40°C
30°C
20°C
10°C
0°C
−10°C
−20°C
−30°C

3-100Aa

6. Find each sum.

$$\begin{array}{r} \$\,2\,4\,9.3\,8 \\ +\ 3\,7\,5.7\,1 \\ \hline \end{array}$$

$$\begin{array}{r} \$\,3\,9.9\,5 \\ +\ 8\,4\,7.9\,5 \\ \hline \end{array}$$

$436.57 + $375.63

7. Mr. Stock had a dozen pencils. He gave half of the pencils to Mary, two to Joy, and the rest to Sidney. How many pencils did he give each child?

Mary _____   Joy _____   Sidney _____

What fractional part of the pencils does Joy have? _____

8. What are the smudged digits?

$8 + 8 + 8 + 8 + 8 + 8 = \text{❂} \times 8$ \qquad $64 + 26 = \text{❂} \times 10$

___ \qquad\qquad\qquad\qquad\qquad ___

$43 + 1\text{❂} = 7 \times 8$ \qquad $6 \times \text{❂} = 300 \div 10$ \qquad $\sqrt{36} = 10 - \text{❂}$

___ \qquad\qquad\qquad ___ \qquad\qquad\qquad\qquad ___

9. Measure the vertical line segment using inches. _____"

Measure the horizontal line segment using millimeters. _____ mm

Measure the oblique line segment using centimeters. _____ cm

10. Complete the patterns. Write the rules.

____ , ____ , ____ , 650, 625, 600, ____ , ____ , ____ Rule: _____

356, 346, 336, ____ , ____ , ____ , ____ , ____ , ____ Rule: _____

____ , ____ , ____ , ____ , ____ , ____ , 64, 72, 80 Rule: _____

3-100Ab

OUR BEAN EXPERIMENT

My name _____   My partner's name _____

Date planted _____

What our plants looked like after 10 days.

Sunny   Date _____   Shady

Height _____ cm   Height _____ cm

At the end of 10 days, summarize what you observed.

_____

_____

_____

_____

_____

_____

_____

_____

Name _____

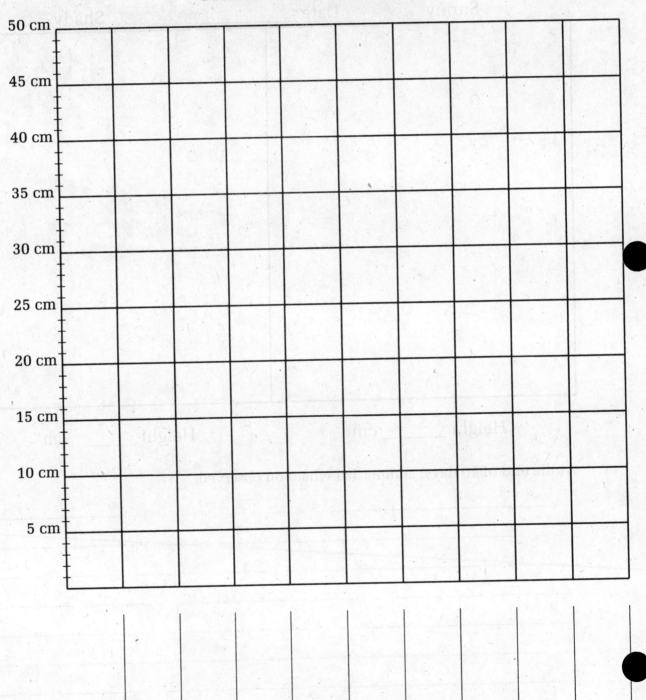

☐ sunny location
☐ shady location

Growth of Two Bean Plants

Dates

Date _____

Sunny   Shady

Height _____ cm   Height _____ cm

Observations: _____

_____

_____

_____

_____

_____

_____

_____

Date _____

Sunny   Shady

Height _____ cm   Height _____ cm

Observations: _____

_____

_____

_____

_____

_____

_____

_____

$$
\begin{array}{r} 2 \\ \times\ 3 \\ \hline \end{array}
\qquad
\begin{array}{r} 7 \\ \times\ 6 \\ \hline \end{array}
\qquad
\begin{array}{r} 4 \\ \times\ 6 \\ \hline \end{array}
\qquad
\begin{array}{r} 5 \\ \times\ 3 \\ \hline \end{array}
\qquad
\begin{array}{r} 6 \\ \times\ 6 \\ \hline \end{array}
$$

$$
\begin{array}{r} 6 \\ \times\ 3 \\ \hline \end{array}
\qquad
\begin{array}{r} 3 \\ \times\ 3 \\ \hline \end{array}
\qquad
\begin{array}{r} 5 \\ \times\ 6 \\ \hline \end{array}
\qquad
\begin{array}{r} 8 \\ \times\ 6 \\ \hline \end{array}
\qquad
\begin{array}{r} 2 \\ \times\ 3 \\ \hline \end{array}
$$

$$
\begin{array}{r} 6 \\ \times\ 6 \\ \hline \end{array}
\qquad
\begin{array}{r} 9 \\ \times\ 3 \\ \hline \end{array}
\qquad
\begin{array}{r} 2 \\ \times\ 6 \\ \hline \end{array}
\qquad
\begin{array}{r} 7 \\ \times\ 3 \\ \hline \end{array}
\qquad
\begin{array}{r} 1 \\ \times\ 6 \\ \hline \end{array}
$$

$$
\begin{array}{r} 8 \\ \times\ 3 \\ \hline \end{array}
\qquad
\begin{array}{r} 0 \\ \times\ 3 \\ \hline \end{array}
\qquad
\begin{array}{r} 9 \\ \times\ 6 \\ \hline \end{array}
\qquad
\begin{array}{r} 3 \\ \times\ 6 \\ \hline \end{array}
\qquad
\begin{array}{r} 4 \\ \times\ 3 \\ \hline \end{array}
$$

$$
\begin{array}{r} 1 \\ \times\ 3 \\ \hline \end{array}
\qquad
\begin{array}{r} 6 \\ \times\ 6 \\ \hline \end{array}
\qquad
\begin{array}{r} 0 \\ \times\ 6 \\ \hline \end{array}
\qquad
\begin{array}{r} 8 \\ \times\ 6 \\ \hline \end{array}
\qquad
\begin{array}{r} 9 \\ \times\ 3 \\ \hline \end{array}
$$

Score: _____

3-100Fa

Name _____

S 8.2

12 − 4	8 − 3	9 − 6	11 − 8	12 − 5
14 − 6	11 − 4	13 − 5	12 − 8	9 − 3
11 − 7	13 − 8	12 − 7	8 − 5	14 − 8
11 − 3	9 − 6	12 − 4	13 − 5	11 − 8
14 − 6	8 − 3	11 − 4	12 − 8	12 − 5

Score: _____

3-101Fa

Name _____ •
(Draw a 120 mm line segment.)

Date _____ •

(Draw a $3\frac{3}{4}$" line segment.)

1. Mr. Brandon sold two hundred seventeen children's tickets and one hundred thirty-five adult tickets for the 6:00 p.m. movie. How many tickets did he sell?

Number sentence _____ Answer _____

The theater has five hundred eighty-five seats. How many more tickets can he sell for the six o'clock show?

Number sentence _____ Answer _____

2. Write 723 in expanded form. _____

3. These are pies. How much pie is left? _____

How much pie was eaten? _____

4. What number is north of 27? _____

What number is east of 7? _____

What number is west of 17? _____

6	7	8
16	17	18
26	27	28

5. What is the smudged digit in each example?

$\begin{array}{r} \$4\,2\,1 \\ +\ 3\,\text{\rlap{⬤}}7 \\ \hline \$7\,6\,8 \end{array}$ _____

$\begin{array}{r} \$2\,6\,3 \\ +\ \text{⬤}\,7\,2 \\ \hline \$6\,3\,5 \end{array}$ _____

$\begin{array}{r} \$5\,2\,5 \\ +\ 4\,0\,\text{⬤} \\ \hline \$9\,3\,1 \end{array}$ _____

6. Write twenty-three thousand, four hundred three using digits. _____

7. Write 31,247 using words. _____

_____

Date _____

1. Mr. Ault sold three hundred twenty-seven children's tickets and two hundred sixteen adult tickets for the 10:00 a.m. movie. How many tickets did he sell?

   Number sentence _____ Answer _____

   The theater has five hundred eighty-five seats. How many more tickets can he sell for the ten o'clock show?

   Number sentence _____ Answer _____

2. Write 509 in expanded form. _____

3. These are pies.
   How much pie is left? _____

   How much pie was eaten? _____

4. What number is south of 8? _____

   What number is west of 27? _____

   What number is north of 18? _____

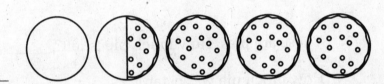

6	7	8
16	17	18
26	27	28

5. What is the smudged digit in each example?

$$\begin{array}{r} \$4\,3\,8 \\ +\ 3\,\blacksquare\,4 \\ \hline \$7\,7\,2 \end{array} \quad\_\_\_\_ \qquad \begin{array}{r} \$6\,7\,9 \\ +\ \blacksquare\,4\,0 \\ \hline \$8\,1\,9 \end{array} \quad\_\_\_\_ \qquad \begin{array}{r} \$2\,\blacksquare\,8 \\ +\ 3\,6\,1 \\ \hline \$5\,8\,9 \end{array} \quad\_\_\_\_$$

6. Write twelve thousand, six hundred thirty using digits. _____

7. Write 48,156 using words. _____

   _____

Name _____

Date _____

PAY TO THE
ORDER OF _____ $ [   ]

_____ DOLLARS

_____

Date _____

PAY TO THE
ORDER OF _____ $ [   ]

_____ DOLLARS

_____

Date _____

PAY TO THE
ORDER OF _____ $ [   ]

_____ DOLLARS

_____

$$
\begin{array}{r} 8 \\ \times\,5 \\ \hline \end{array}
\qquad
\begin{array}{r} 7 \\ \times\,6 \\ \hline \end{array}
\qquad
\begin{array}{r} 3 \\ \times\,8 \\ \hline \end{array}
\qquad
\begin{array}{r} 4 \\ \times\,4 \\ \hline \end{array}
\qquad
\begin{array}{r} 6 \\ \times\,0 \\ \hline \end{array}
$$

$$
\begin{array}{r} 2 \\ \times\,3 \\ \hline \end{array}
\qquad
\begin{array}{r} 8 \\ \times\,6 \\ \hline \end{array}
\qquad
\begin{array}{r} 2 \\ \times\,6 \\ \hline \end{array}
\qquad
\begin{array}{r} 9 \\ \times\,7 \\ \hline \end{array}
\qquad
\begin{array}{r} 10 \\ \times\,4 \\ \hline \end{array}
$$

$$
\begin{array}{r} 6 \\ \times\,6 \\ \hline \end{array}
\qquad
\begin{array}{r} 6 \\ \times\,4 \\ \hline \end{array}
\qquad
\begin{array}{r} 3 \\ \times\,3 \\ \hline \end{array}
\qquad
\begin{array}{r} 9 \\ \times\,6 \\ \hline \end{array}
\qquad
\begin{array}{r} 7 \\ \times\,8 \\ \hline \end{array}
$$

$$
\begin{array}{r} 7 \\ \times\,3 \\ \hline \end{array}
\qquad
\begin{array}{r} 5 \\ \times\,6 \\ \hline \end{array}
\qquad
\begin{array}{r} 4 \\ \times\,8 \\ \hline \end{array}
\qquad
\begin{array}{r} 6 \\ \times\,3 \\ \hline \end{array}
\qquad
\begin{array}{r} 10 \\ \times\,5 \\ \hline \end{array}
$$

$$
\begin{array}{r} 8 \\ \times\,8 \\ \hline \end{array}
\qquad
\begin{array}{r} 3 \\ \times\,5 \\ \hline \end{array}
\qquad
\begin{array}{r} 1 \\ \times\,6 \\ \hline \end{array}
\qquad
\begin{array}{r} 7 \\ \times\,7 \\ \hline \end{array}
\qquad
\begin{array}{r} 9 \\ \times\,2 \\ \hline \end{array}
$$

Score: _____

Name _____

(Draw a $4\frac{1}{2}$" line segment.)

Date _____

(Draw a 6 cm 4 mm line segment.)

1. There are twenty children in Mrs. Tyska's class. Half of the children went to the art room. How many children went to the art room?

   Number sentence _____ Answer _____

   They brought back four sets of paints each. How many sets of paints did they bring back altogether?

   Number sentence _____ Answer _____

2. Write 250 in expanded form. _____

3. Draw a bar graph to show the children's favorite multiplication facts.

	Number of children
twos	35
fours	18
sevens	42

   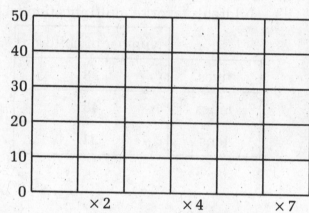

   How many more children chose multiplying by seven than multiplying by two?

   Answer _____

4. Label this compass. You are facing east and you point to the right.

   In which direction are you pointing? _____

5. The Board of Education has fuel bills for $6219.37, $729.35, and $1623.63. Find how much they owe for fuel and show how they will write this amount on a check.

   _____ DOLLARS

3-102Wa

1. There were eighteen children at the party. Half of the children ate chocolate cupcakes. How many children ate chocolate cupcakes?

   Number sentence _____ Answer _____

   They ate 3 cupcakes each. How many chocolate cupcakes did they eat altogether?

   Number sentence _____ Answer _____

2. Write 148 in expanded form. _____

3. Draw a bar graph to show the children's favorite multiplication facts.

	Number of children
fives	28
nines	45
tens	31

   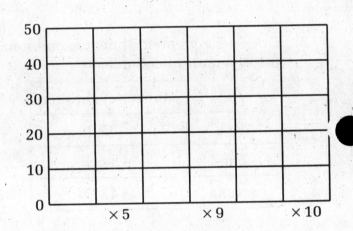

   How many more children chose multiplying by ten than multiplying by five? _____

4. Label this compass. You are facing north and you point to the left.

   In which direction are you pointing? _____

5. The Board of Education has food bills for $829.37, $1,215.16, and $2,399.20. Find how much they owe for food. Show how they will write this amount on a check.

   DOLLARS

   _____

Name _____

Today's Date is _____

Today's Pattern _____
_____

Today's Problem

Coin Cup

Q	D	N	P	Total Coins

Today's Date is _____

Today's Pattern _____
_____

Today's Problem

Coin Cup

Q	D	N	P	Total Coins

Today's Date is _____

Today's Pattern _____
_____

Today's Problem

Coin Cup

Q	D	N	P	Total Coins

Today's Date is _____

Today's Pattern _____
_____

Today's Problem

Coin Cup

Q	D	N	P	Total Coins

Today's Date is _____

Today's Pattern _____
_____

Today's Problem

Coin Cup

Q	D	N	P	Total Coins

$$\begin{array}{r} 8 \\ \times\ 5 \\ \hline \end{array} \qquad \begin{array}{r} 7 \\ \times\ 6 \\ \hline \end{array} \qquad \begin{array}{r} 3 \\ \times\ 8 \\ \hline \end{array} \qquad \begin{array}{r} 4 \\ \times\ 4 \\ \hline \end{array} \qquad \begin{array}{r} 6 \\ \times\ 0 \\ \hline \end{array}$$

$$\begin{array}{r} 2 \\ \times\ 3 \\ \hline \end{array} \qquad \begin{array}{r} 8 \\ \times\ 6 \\ \hline \end{array} \qquad \begin{array}{r} 2 \\ \times\ 6 \\ \hline \end{array} \qquad \begin{array}{r} 9 \\ \times\ 7 \\ \hline \end{array} \qquad \begin{array}{r} 10 \\ \times\ 4 \\ \hline \end{array}$$

$$\begin{array}{r} 6 \\ \times\ 6 \\ \hline \end{array} \qquad \begin{array}{r} 6 \\ \times\ 4 \\ \hline \end{array} \qquad \begin{array}{r} 3 \\ \times\ 3 \\ \hline \end{array} \qquad \begin{array}{r} 9 \\ \times\ 6 \\ \hline \end{array} \qquad \begin{array}{r} 7 \\ \times\ 8 \\ \hline \end{array}$$

$$\begin{array}{r} 7 \\ \times\ 3 \\ \hline \end{array} \qquad \begin{array}{r} 5 \\ \times\ 6 \\ \hline \end{array} \qquad \begin{array}{r} 4 \\ \times\ 8 \\ \hline \end{array} \qquad \begin{array}{r} 6 \\ \times\ 3 \\ \hline \end{array} \qquad \begin{array}{r} 10 \\ \times\ 5 \\ \hline \end{array}$$

$$\begin{array}{r} 8 \\ \times\ 8 \\ \hline \end{array} \qquad \begin{array}{r} 3 \\ \times\ 5 \\ \hline \end{array} \qquad \begin{array}{r} 1 \\ \times\ 6 \\ \hline \end{array} \qquad \begin{array}{r} 7 \\ \times\ 7 \\ \hline \end{array} \qquad \begin{array}{r} 9 \\ \times\ 2 \\ \hline \end{array}$$

Score: _____

3-103Fa

Name _____ •

(Draw a $2\frac{1}{2}$" line segment. Measure it using millimeters. _____ mm) **LESSON 103A**

Date _____ • **Math 3**

(Draw a line segment 2" longer than the name line segment. How long is it? _____")

1. Each of the six girls used seven books. Each of the five boys used eight books.

    How many books did the girls use? _____

    How many books did the boys use? _____

    How many books did they use altogether? _____

2. Show quarter past two on the clocks.   Show quarter of seven on the clocks.

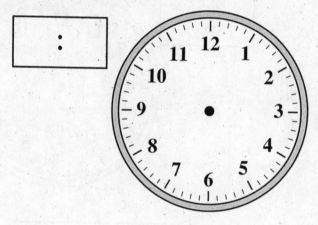   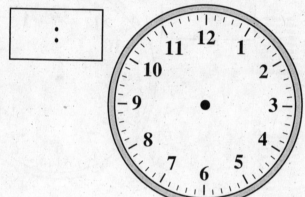

3. Draw a rectangle that has a length of 30 mm
    and a width of 15 mm. Label the sides.

    What is the perimeter? _____

4. I have 9 thousand-dollar bills, 3 one-dollar bills, 7 hundred-dollar bills, 6 pennies,
    and 2 dimes.

    How much money do I have? _____

5. Find each difference.

    $592 - 48 =$ _____ $451 - 230 =$ _____ $367 - 258 =$ _____

Name _____ **LESSON 103B**
                                         Math 3
Date _____

1. Each of the four large dogs ate 9 dog biscuits. Each of the seven small dogs ate 5 dog biscuits.

   How many dog biscuits did the large dogs eat? _____

   How many dog biscuits did the small dogs eat? _____

   How many dog biscuits did they eat altogether? _____

2. Show quarter past eight on the clocks.   Show quarter of four on the clocks.

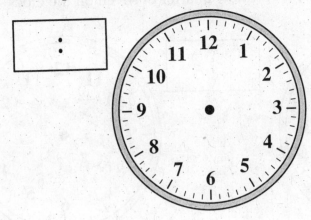   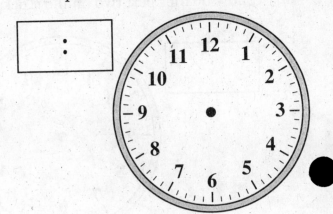

3. What is the perimeter of the rectangle?

   _____

   21 mm [rectangle] 43 mm

4. I have 5 hundred-dollar bills, 2 ten-dollar bills, 6 thousand-dollar bills, and 8 pennies.

   How much money do I have? _____

5. Find each difference.

   671 − 39 = _____   358 − 179 = _____   245 − 190 = _____

Name _____

Prize 1 _____

Money to spend _____

Cost of Prize #1 _____

Money left over _____

Were you right?
Did you win the prize?

Yes ☐   No ☐

Prize 2 _____

Money to spend _____

Cost of Prize #2 _____

Money left over _____

Were you right?
Did you win the prize?

Yes ☐   No ☐

Prize 3 _____

Money to spend _____

Cost of Prize #3 _____

Money left over _____

Were you right?
Did you win the prize?

Yes ☐   No ☐

Prize 4 _____

Money to spend _____

Cost of Prize #4 _____

Money left over _____

Were you right?
Did you win the prize?

Yes ☐   No ☐

Do you want the:

Prizes? _____

Money? _____
($75 for each prize)

What is the total value of the prizes you won?

Total ☐

$$
\begin{array}{r} 8 \\ \times\ 5 \\ \hline \end{array}
\qquad
\begin{array}{r} 7 \\ \times\ 6 \\ \hline \end{array}
\qquad
\begin{array}{r} 3 \\ \times\ 8 \\ \hline \end{array}
\qquad
\begin{array}{r} 4 \\ \times\ 4 \\ \hline \end{array}
\qquad
\begin{array}{r} 6 \\ \times\ 0 \\ \hline \end{array}
$$

$$
\begin{array}{r} 2 \\ \times\ 3 \\ \hline \end{array}
\qquad
\begin{array}{r} 8 \\ \times\ 6 \\ \hline \end{array}
\qquad
\begin{array}{r} 2 \\ \times\ 6 \\ \hline \end{array}
\qquad
\begin{array}{r} 9 \\ \times\ 7 \\ \hline \end{array}
\qquad
\begin{array}{r} 10 \\ \times\ 4 \\ \hline \end{array}
$$

$$
\begin{array}{r} 6 \\ \times\ 6 \\ \hline \end{array}
\qquad
\begin{array}{r} 6 \\ \times\ 4 \\ \hline \end{array}
\qquad
\begin{array}{r} 3 \\ \times\ 3 \\ \hline \end{array}
\qquad
\begin{array}{r} 9 \\ \times\ 6 \\ \hline \end{array}
\qquad
\begin{array}{r} 7 \\ \times\ 8 \\ \hline \end{array}
$$

$$
\begin{array}{r} 7 \\ \times\ 3 \\ \hline \end{array}
\qquad
\begin{array}{r} 5 \\ \times\ 6 \\ \hline \end{array}
\qquad
\begin{array}{r} 4 \\ \times\ 8 \\ \hline \end{array}
\qquad
\begin{array}{r} 6 \\ \times\ 3 \\ \hline \end{array}
\qquad
\begin{array}{r} 10 \\ \times\ 5 \\ \hline \end{array}
$$

$$
\begin{array}{r} 8 \\ \times\ 8 \\ \hline \end{array}
\qquad
\begin{array}{r} 3 \\ \times\ 5 \\ \hline \end{array}
\qquad
\begin{array}{r} 1 \\ \times\ 6 \\ \hline \end{array}
\qquad
\begin{array}{r} 7 \\ \times\ 7 \\ \hline \end{array}
\qquad
\begin{array}{r} 9 \\ \times\ 2 \\ \hline \end{array}
$$

Score: _____

Name •

(Draw a $4\frac{3}{4}''$ line segment.)

Date •

(Draw a 9 cm line segment.)

1. Jason does ten situps each night. How many situps will he do during the month of March?

   Number sentence _____ Answer _____

2. Show 4 ways to make 80¢.

Q	D	N	P	Total Coins

   What coins would you use to make 80¢ using the fewest number of coins? Draw the coins.

3. Find the answers. Check each answer by adding.

   $$\$9\,0\,3 \quad -\ 7\,2\,9$$

   $$\$6\,0\,0 \quad -\ 1\,5\,8$$

   $$\$5\,4\,0 \quad -\ 3\,1\,7$$

4. There are eight people in line. You are third.

   How many people are before you? _____ What fractional part is that? _____

   Each person takes a half hour.
   How long will you have to wait for your turn? _____

5. Write $51,240.16 as you would on a check.

   _____ DOLLARS

6. Use the correct comparison symbol (>, <, or =).

   62×1000 ☐ 584×100 $\sqrt{64} + \sqrt{49}$ ☐ $150 \div 10$

   $\$2649.37 + \$3457.48$ ☐ $\$4226.93 + \$1877.08$

3-104Wa

Name _____

Date _____

1. Each evening Michelle reads 10 pages of a book. How many pages will she read during the month of April?

   Number sentence _____   Answer _____

2. Show 4 ways to make 90¢.

Q	D	N	P	Total Coins

   What coins would you use to make 90¢ using the fewest number of coins? Draw the coins.

3. Find the answers. Check each answer by adding.

   $$\$7\,0\,4 \\ -\ 4\,1\,7$$ $$\$5\,0\,0 \\ -\ 2\,3\,7$$ $$\$6\,7\,0 \\ -\ 1\,4\,6$$

4. There are eight people in line. You are fourth.

   How many people are before you? _____   What fractional part is that? _____

   Each person takes a half hour.
   How long will you have to wait for your turn? _____

5. Write $70,309.27 as you would on a check.

   _____ DOLLARS

6. Use the correct comparison symbol (>, <, or =).

   165×100 ☐ 17×1000 $\sqrt{81} - \sqrt{16}$ ☐ $8 \times 3 - 20$

   $\$29,517.38 + \$13,438.54$ ☐ $\$31,587.20 + \$12,614.35$

Name •

(Draw a $3\frac{1}{4}$" line segment.)

Date •

(Draw a 6 cm 5 mm line segment.)

Gifts	
basketball	$23.78
game	$18.25
book	$15.95

1. Lorena saved $50.00 from her paper route.
   She bought a basketball and a book.
   How much did she spend?

   Number sentence _____

   Answer _____

   Does she have enough money to buy all three gifts? _____

2. How many days are in the last 3 months of the year? _____

3. It's afternoon.
   What time is it? _____

4. Show 4 different ways to make 70¢.

Q	D	N	P	Total Coins

5. Write your teacher's last name in the box.

   What fractional part of this word is vowels? _____

   What fractional part of this word is consonants? _____

6. Find the answers.

   $$\begin{array}{r} 57 \\ -28 \\ \hline \end{array}$$

   $$\begin{array}{r} 94 \\ -63 \\ \hline \end{array}$$

   $$\begin{array}{r} 83 \\ -46 \\ \hline \end{array}$$

7. Shade the graph to show how many points each child scored.

Child	Points
James	45
Scott	
Alex	30
Beth	39

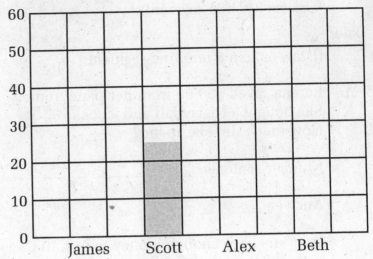

8. Answer these questions using the information in question 7.

About how many points did Scott score? _____

How many points did James and Alex score together? _____

How many more points than Alex did Beth score? _____

Write the children's names in order from the one who scored the most points to the one who scored the fewest points.

_____ _____ _____ _____

9. Use the correct comparison symbol.

$\sqrt{16}$ + 3 ☐ 70 ÷ 10   47 × 10 ☐ 138 + 335

6 × 8 ☐ 17 + 38   4 × 9 ☐ 1 + 5 + 8 + 2 + 6 + 7 + 5 + 4

10. Find the sums.

$246.25 + $185.39 $512.63 + $69.72 + $104.16

7	9	5	2	9
× 9	× 3	× 9	× 9	× 8

9	9	6	9	3
× 4	× 0	× 9	× 1	× 9

2	9	9	9	0
× 9	× 5	× 9	× 4	× 9

9	9	9	7	4
× 8	× 6	× 3	× 9	× 9

5	9	9	9	1
× 9	× 0	× 2	× 9	× 9

Score: _____

Name ●
(Draw a 115 mm line segment.)

Date ●

(Draw a 12 cm line segment. Which line segment is longer? _____)

1. Nicki reads five pages of a book each morning and three pages each evening. How many pages will she read in one week?

    Number sentence _____ Answer _____

2. Althea was born in 1967, Terrel was born in 1978, and Skyla was born in 1983. How old will each person be on this year's birthday?

    Althea _____   Terrell _____   Skyla _____

3. Measure each line segment using inches.

    ●————————● _____

    ●————————————————● _____

4. Alicia, Barry, Fred, and Janet will share twenty-four peanuts. Draw a napkin for each child. Draw the peanuts on each child's napkin.

    How many peanuts will each child receive? _____

5. Pretend you are the teacher. Correct this paper. Write the correct answers below the examples with the wrong answers.

    1. What is the perimeter of the rectangle around these problems? ___26 cm___

    2. What time is shown on the clock? ___3:30___

    3. Find the answers.

    $$\begin{array}{r} 145 \\ -\ 29 \\ \hline 126 \end{array} \qquad \begin{array}{r} 400 \\ -\ 172 \\ \hline 372 \end{array} \qquad \begin{array}{r} \$4{,}256.23 \\ +\ 6{,}192.58 \\ \hline \$8{,}648.81 \end{array}$$

3-105Wa

Name _____

Date _____

1. Sam rides his bicycle two miles each morning and five miles each afternoon. How many miles will he ride in one week?

   Number sentence _____ Answer _____

2. Bonnie was born in 1986, Joanna was born in 1958, and Helen was born in 1940. How old will each person be on this year's birthday?

   Bonnie _____   Joanna _____   Helen _____

3. Today's number is _____. Write four number sentences. (Use addition, subtraction, multiplication, and division.)

   _____   _____

   _____   _____

4. Joel, Holly, and Irving will share eighteen small donuts. Draw a plate for each child. Draw the donuts on each child's plate.

   How many donuts will each child receive? _____

5. Pretend you are the teacher. Correct this paper. Write the correct answers below the examples with the wrong answers.

   1. What is the perimeter of this small rectangle? <u>80 mm</u>

   2. What time is shown on the clock? <u>7:35</u>

   23 mm

   3. Write 208 in expanded form.

      <u>200 + 8</u>

   12 mm

   4. Find the answers.

   ```
    3 0 0        3 7 1        $ 3 , 2 9 7.5 8
   - 1 6 9      -  8 0       + 4 , 8 1 6.3 1
   -------      -------      ----------------
    1 4 1        3 9 1        $ 8 , 1 0 3.8 9
   ```

$$\begin{array}{r} 7 \\ \times\ 9 \\ \hline \end{array} \qquad \begin{array}{r} 9 \\ \times\ 3 \\ \hline \end{array} \qquad \begin{array}{r} 5 \\ \times\ 9 \\ \hline \end{array} \qquad \begin{array}{r} 2 \\ \times\ 9 \\ \hline \end{array} \qquad \begin{array}{r} 9 \\ \times\ 8 \\ \hline \end{array}$$

$$\begin{array}{r} 9 \\ \times\ 4 \\ \hline \end{array} \qquad \begin{array}{r} 9 \\ \times\ 0 \\ \hline \end{array} \qquad \begin{array}{r} 6 \\ \times\ 9 \\ \hline \end{array} \qquad \begin{array}{r} 9 \\ \times\ 1 \\ \hline \end{array} \qquad \begin{array}{r} 3 \\ \times\ 9 \\ \hline \end{array}$$

$$\begin{array}{r} 2 \\ \times\ 9 \\ \hline \end{array} \qquad \begin{array}{r} 9 \\ \times\ 5 \\ \hline \end{array} \qquad \begin{array}{r} 9 \\ \times\ 9 \\ \hline \end{array} \qquad \begin{array}{r} 9 \\ \times\ 4 \\ \hline \end{array} \qquad \begin{array}{r} 0 \\ \times\ 9 \\ \hline \end{array}$$

$$\begin{array}{r} 9 \\ \times\ 8 \\ \hline \end{array} \qquad \begin{array}{r} 9 \\ \times\ 6 \\ \hline \end{array} \qquad \begin{array}{r} 9 \\ \times\ 3 \\ \hline \end{array} \qquad \begin{array}{r} 7 \\ \times\ 9 \\ \hline \end{array} \qquad \begin{array}{r} 4 \\ \times\ 9 \\ \hline \end{array}$$

$$\begin{array}{r} 5 \\ \times\ 9 \\ \hline \end{array} \qquad \begin{array}{r} 9 \\ \times\ 0 \\ \hline \end{array} \qquad \begin{array}{r} 9 \\ \times\ 2 \\ \hline \end{array} \qquad \begin{array}{r} 9 \\ \times\ 9 \\ \hline \end{array} \qquad \begin{array}{r} 1 \\ \times\ 9 \\ \hline \end{array}$$

Score: _____

3-106Fa

16	7	15	9	14
− 9	− 2	− 6	− 5	− 9

10	12	16	8	13
− 4	− 9	− 7	− 6	− 4

12	11	16	13	7
− 3	− 6	− 8	− 9	− 6

7	15	.14	15	10
− 4	− 9	− 5	− 8	− 6

12	10	11	7	17
− 6	− 3	− 9	− 1	− 9

Score: _____

Name

(Draw a $3\frac{1}{2}$" line segment.)

Date

(Draw a 72 mm line segment.)

1. Jason made a 3-minute call to Area 3. How much did the call cost? _____

	Area 1	Area 2	Area 3
First minute	4¢	5¢	6¢
Additional minutes	1¢	2¢	3¢

2. Write fifty-eight thousand, six hundred nine using digits. _____

3. Write $35,210.63 as you would on a check.

_____ DOLLARS

4. Fill in the missing addends.

13 + ☐ = 100   71 + ☐ = 100   54 + ☐ = 100

5. Annette, Ebony, and Donna will share 15 markers. Draw the markers on the children's desks.

☐ ☐ ☐

How many markers will each child receive? _____

What fractional part of the markers will each child have? _____

6. Put these numbers in order from least to greatest.

500, 248, 352, 384, 296   ____ ____ ____ ____ ____

Find the sum of the three smallest numbers. _____

Subtract the smallest number from the greatest number. _____

7. Fill in the correct number.

$\sqrt{9}$ − ☐ = 6 × 2 − 10   ☐ + 10 = 160 ÷ 10

3 × ☐ = 5 × 3   8 × 3 = ☐ × 4

Name _____

Date _____

1. Paul made a 5-minute call to Area 1. How much did the call cost? _____

	Area 1	Area 2	Area 3
First minute	4¢	5¢	6¢
Additional minutes	1¢	2¢	3¢

2. Write sixty-one thousand, two hundred seventy using digits. _____

3. Write $27,186.50 as you would on a check.

   _____ DOLLARS

4. Fill in the missing addends.

   $82 + \boxed{} = 100$ $26 + \boxed{} = 100$ $59 + \boxed{} = 100$

5. Alan, Lance, Ted, and Kyle will share 20 markers.
   Draw the markers on the children's desks.

   How many markers will each child receive? _____

   What fractional part of the markers will each child have? _____

6. Put these numbers in order from least to greatest.

   | 478, 345, 362, 600, 275 | _____ _____ _____ _____ _____

   Find the sum of the three smallest numbers. _____

   Subtract the smallest number from the greatest number. _____

7. Fill in the correct number.

   $\sqrt{25} - \boxed{} = 3 \times 8 - 20$ $\boxed{} + 10 = 360 \div 10$

   $4 \times \boxed{} = 9 \times 4$ $9 \times 2 = 3 \times \boxed{}$

Name _____

Today's Problem

Coin Cup

Q	D	N	P	Total Coins
				___

Today's Date is _____

Today's Pattern _____

_____

Today's Problem

Coin Cup

Q	D	N	P	Total Coins
				___

Today's Date is _____

Today's Pattern _____

_____

Today's Problem

Coin Cup

Q	D	N	P	Total Coins
				___

Today's Date is _____

Today's Pattern _____

_____

Today's Problem

Coin Cup

Q	D	N	P	Total Coins
				___

Today's Date is _____

Today's Pattern _____

_____

Today's Problem

Coin Cup

Q	D	N	P	Total Coins
				___

Today's Date is _____

Today's Pattern _____

_____

3-*R1Ma

Making Change From $1.00

Counting back change

Cost of item	Change from $1.00	Coins used for the change				Counting back change
		Q	D	N	P	
						Say
						Say
						Say
						Say
						Say
						Say
						Say
						Say

12 − 4	8 − 3	9 − 6	11 − 8	12 − 5
14 − 6	11 − 4	13 − 5	12 − 8	9 − 3
11 − 7	13 − 8	12 − 7	8 − 5	14 − 8
11 − 3	9 − 6	12 − 4	13 − 5	11 − 8
14 − 6	8 − 3	11 − 4	12 − 8	12 − 5

Score: _____

1. John weeded Mr. Hill's large garden and trimmed 6 of his shrubs. How much will John charge Mr. Hill?

    Number sentence _____

    Answer _____

John's Lawn Service	
Mowing Lawns:	
small $5.00	large $8.00
Weeding Gardens:	
small $3.00	large $5.00
Trimming Shrubs:	50¢ each
Senior Citizen Discount:	$1.00

2. Fill in the missing addends.

    $12 + \boxed{} = 100$ $33 + \boxed{} = 100$

3. Show quarter of ten on the clocks.

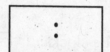

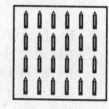

4. The cost of a marker is 59¢.

    How much change will you receive from $1.00? _____

5. Each box has 24 pencils. Divide the first box in half. Divide the second box into thirds. Divide the last box into fourths. Find each answer.

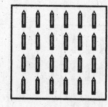 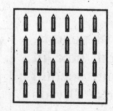 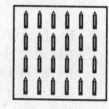

    $\frac{1}{2}$ of 24 = _____ $\frac{1}{3}$ of 24 = _____ $\frac{1}{4}$ of 24 = _____

6. Someone found the difference between $600 and $143 like this.

    $$\$\overset{5}{\cancel{6}}\overset{1}{\cancel{0}}\overset{1}{\cancel{0}}$$
    $$-\ 1\ 4\ 3$$
    $$\overline{\$4\ 6\ 7}$$

    Why is this not correct? _____

    _____

    _____

    _____

Correct Answer

Name _____

Date _____

1. John mowed Mr. Smith's lawn and weeded his garden. Mr. Smith, who is a senior citizen, has a small garden and a small lawn. How much will John charge Mr. Smith?

   Number sentence _____

   Answer _____

John's Lawn Service	
Mowing Lawns:	
small $5.00	large $8.00
Weeding Gardens:	
small $3.00	large $5.00
Trimming Shrubs:	50¢ each
Senior Citizen Discount:	$1.00

2. Fill in the missing addends.

   $44 +$ 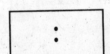 $= 100$ $84 +$ $\boxed{}$ $= 100$

3. Show quarter of four on the clocks.

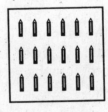

4. The cost of an eraser is 29¢.

   How much change will you receive from $1.00? _____

5. Each box has 18 pencils. Divide the first box in half. Divide the second box into thirds. Divide the last box into sixths. Find each answer.

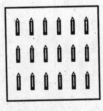   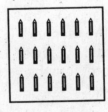   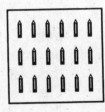

   $\frac{1}{2}$ of 18 = _____ $\frac{1}{3}$ of 18 = _____ $\frac{1}{6}$ of 18 = _____

6. Someone found the difference between $400 and $236 like this.

   $$\begin{array}{r} \$400 \\ -\ 236 \\ \hline \$174 \end{array}$$

   Why is this not correct? _____

   _____

   _____

   _____

Correct Answer

3-107Wb

A

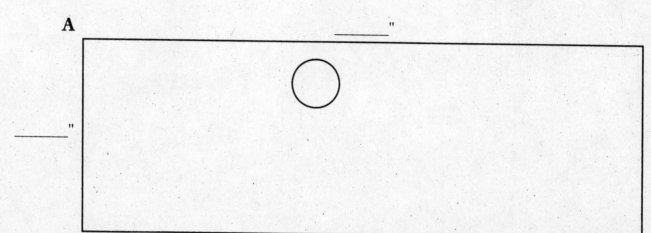

_____ "

_____ "

B

_____ "

_____ "

D

_____ "

_____ "

C

_____ "

_____ "

$$
\begin{array}{r} 16 \\ -\ 9 \\ \hline \end{array}
\qquad
\begin{array}{r} 7 \\ -\ 2 \\ \hline \end{array}
\qquad
\begin{array}{r} 15 \\ -\ 6 \\ \hline \end{array}
\qquad
\begin{array}{r} 9 \\ -\ 5 \\ \hline \end{array}
\qquad
\begin{array}{r} 14 \\ -\ 9 \\ \hline \end{array}
$$

$$
\begin{array}{r} 10 \\ -\ 4 \\ \hline \end{array}
\qquad
\begin{array}{r} 12 \\ -\ 9 \\ \hline \end{array}
\qquad
\begin{array}{r} 16 \\ -\ 7 \\ \hline \end{array}
\qquad
\begin{array}{r} 8 \\ -\ 6 \\ \hline \end{array}
\qquad
\begin{array}{r} 13 \\ -\ 4 \\ \hline \end{array}
$$

$$
\begin{array}{r} 12 \\ -\ 3 \\ \hline \end{array}
\qquad
\begin{array}{r} 11 \\ -\ 6 \\ \hline \end{array}
\qquad
\begin{array}{r} 16 \\ -\ 8 \\ \hline \end{array}
\qquad
\begin{array}{r} 13 \\ -\ 9 \\ \hline \end{array}
\qquad
\begin{array}{r} 7 \\ -\ 6 \\ \hline \end{array}
$$

$$
\begin{array}{r} 7 \\ -\ 4 \\ \hline \end{array}
\qquad
\begin{array}{r} 15 \\ -\ 9 \\ \hline \end{array}
\qquad
\begin{array}{r} 14 \\ -\ 5 \\ \hline \end{array}
\qquad
\begin{array}{r} 15 \\ -\ 8 \\ \hline \end{array}
\qquad
\begin{array}{r} 10 \\ -\ 6 \\ \hline \end{array}
$$

$$
\begin{array}{r} 12 \\ -\ 6 \\ \hline \end{array}
\qquad
\begin{array}{r} 10 \\ -\ 3 \\ \hline \end{array}
\qquad
\begin{array}{r} 11 \\ -\ 9 \\ \hline \end{array}
\qquad
\begin{array}{r} 7 \\ -\ 1 \\ \hline \end{array}
\qquad
\begin{array}{r} 17 \\ -\ 9 \\ \hline \end{array}
$$

Score: _____

Name •
    (Draw a 7 cm 6 mm line segment.)

Date •

    (Draw a congruent line segment. Measure it using millimeters. _____)

1. Use the digit cards to write an even number between 587 and 624.

_____

2. What will be the date thirteen days from today? _____

3. Find the area of each rectangle.

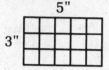
5"
3"

_____ square inches

7"
4"

_____ square inches

4. Draw line segments to show the following lengths.

$5\frac{3}{4}$" •

$1\frac{1}{4}$" •

5. Marcus used $1\frac{3}{4}$ pieces of poster board. Color the rectangles to show how much poster board he used.

How much poster board is left? _____

6. School began at quarter of nine. Show the time on the clock.

Write the digital time. _____

7. Find the answers.

$700 − $319 $667 − $293 $4,921.68 + $469.57

Name _____ **LESSON 108B**

Date _____ *Math 3*

1. Use the digit cards to write an odd number between 294 and 376.

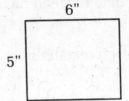

   _____

2. What will be the date eight days from today? _____

3. Find the area of each rectangle.

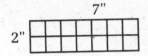

7"

2"

_____ square inches

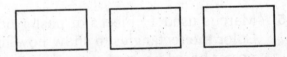

6"

5"

_____ square inches

4. Complete the number patterns. Find the rules.

   60, _____ , 70, _____ , 80, _____ , 90, _____ , 100, _____ , 110 Rule: _____

   513, 511, 509, _____ , _____ , _____ , _____ , _____ , _____ Rule: _____

5. Sheryl used $2\frac{1}{3}$ pieces of poster board. Color the rectangles to show how much poster board she used.

   How much poster board is left? _____

6. School ends at quarter past three. Show the time on the clock.

   Write the digital time. _____

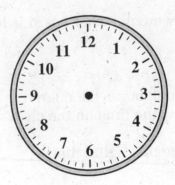

7. Find the answers.

   $800 − $381 $391 − $168 $2,356.64 + $3,917.57

Name _____

A

difference

larger

smaller

_____

_____

B

difference

larger

smaller

_____

_____

C

difference

larger

smaller

_____

_____

D

difference

larger

smaller

_____

_____

E

difference

larger

smaller

_____

_____

F

difference

larger

smaller

_____

_____

Name _____   Score: _____

7 − 1	10 − 4	9 − 0	16 − 9	5 − 4	12 − 6	9 − 7	11 − 3	8 − 2	6 − 6
9 − 4	6 − 3	11 − 6	10 − 2	6 − 1	12 − 8	2 − 0	9 − 3	7 − 2	6 − 5
5 − 5	11 − 4	4 − 2	15 − 9	8 − 0	10 − 6	14 − 5	9 − 9	7 − 6	12 − 7
9 − 5	17 − 9	8 − 4	13 − 8	9 − 2	11 − 5	15 − 6	5 − 1	8 − 5	16 − 8
8 − 6	11 − 7	1 − 0	7 − 3	9 − 6	4 − 3	17 − 8	10 − 5	12 − 4	13 − 7
8 − 3	16 − 7	10 − 3	4 − 1	6 − 2	13 − 5	7 − 0	14 − 9	11 − 2	10 − 8
13 − 9	10 − 7	18 − 9	14 − 6	1 − 1	12 − 3	7 − 5	4 − 1	11 − 8	7 − 7
2 − 2	12 − 5	3 − 1	15 − 7	10 − 1	6 − 0	13 − 4	5 − 2	9 − 8	3 − 0
11 − 9	7 − 6	13 − 6	3 − 3	14 − 8	9 − 1	6 − 4	12 − 9	7 − 4	8 − 7
4 − 4	15 − 8	3 − 2	5 − 0	5 − 3	8 − 8	14 − 7	10 − 9	0 − 0	8 − 1

Name _____ •
(Draw a $4\frac{1}{2}$" line segment.)

Date _____ •

(Draw a 70 mm line segment. How many inches long is the date line? _____)

1. Teddy's birthday is 9 days from today. What is the date of his birthday? _____

   He was born in 1982. How old will he be on his birthday? _____

2. What fractional part of the months of the year begin with the letter J? _____

3. Find the area of each rectangle.

   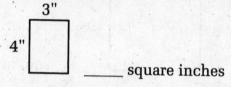
   _____ square inches

   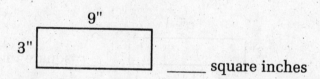
   _____ square inches

4. Write the digital time for each of these clocks. Write the time using words on the line below each clock.

   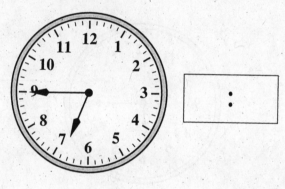

   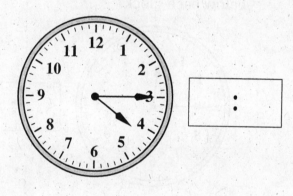

   _____   _____

5. Find each answer.

   $756 − $248 $941 − $308 $37.48 + $259.79

6. Use the correct comparison symbol (>, <, or =).

   6 × 9 ☐ 74 − 30   48 + 15 ☐ 9 × 7 $\frac{1}{2}$ of 40 ☐ 9 × 3

Name _____

Date _____

1. Stephanie's sister had a birthday a week ago.

   What was the date of her birthday? _____

   She was born in 1986. How old is her sister? _____

2. What fractional part of the days of the week begin with the letter T? _____

3. Find the area of each rectangle.

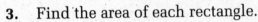

   _____ square inches   _____ square inches

4. Write the digital time for each of these clocks. Write the time using words on the line below each clock.

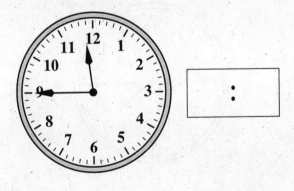   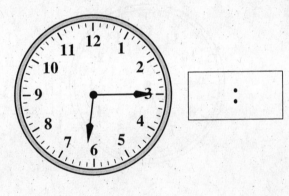

   _____   _____

5. Find each answer.

   $175 − $29 $341 − $290 $143.97 + $86.29

6. Use the correct comparison symbol (>, <, or =).

   $\sqrt{64} + \sqrt{81}$ ☐ 9 × 2   360 ÷ 10 ☐ 4 × 9   8 × 6 + 20 ☐ 9 × 7

Name ●————————————————————————————●
(Measure this line segment using millimeters. _____ mm)

Date ●————————————————————●
(Measure this line segment in centimeters. _____ cm.)

1. Tim walks his dog 3 times a day. How many times will he walk his dog in one week?

   Number sentence _____ Answer _____

   How many times will he walk his dog in 100 days?

   Number sentence _____ Answer _____

2. Tim has an appointment for his dog to visit the vet 10 days from today.

   What is the date of the appointment? _____

3. Measure this line segment using inches.

   ●————————————————————————————● _____

   Draw a $2\frac{3}{4}''$ line segment. ●

4. Write each number in expanded form.

   629 _____

   507 _____

5. It's three forty-two in the afternoon.

   Show the time on the clock.

   Write the time using digits. _____

   What time was it one hour ago? _____

3-110Aa

6. Fill in the missing numbers.

$$\begin{array}{r} 8 \\ \times\ 6 \\ \hline \square \end{array} \qquad \begin{array}{r} \square \\ \times\ 7 \\ \hline 63 \end{array} \qquad \begin{array}{r} \square \\ \times\ 9 \\ \hline 36 \end{array} \qquad \begin{array}{r} 8 \\ \times\ \square \\ \hline 56 \end{array} \qquad \begin{array}{r} \square \\ \times\ 4 \\ \hline 28 \end{array} \qquad \begin{array}{r} 4 \\ \times\ 3 \\ \hline \square \end{array} \qquad \begin{array}{r} 6 \\ \times\ \square \\ \hline 18 \end{array} \qquad \begin{array}{r} \square \\ \times\ 5 \\ \hline 40 \end{array}$$

7. Label the compass.

A	B	C
D	E	F
G	H	I

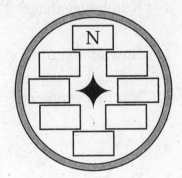

What letter is south of D? _____

What letter is west of H? _____

What letter is southeast of E? _____

8. Carol, Martha, George, Myrtle, and Colleen will share twenty cookies. Draw a plate for each child. Show how the children will share the cookies.

How many cookies will each child receive? _____

9. Jill Gentry bought a television set for $384.75, a bike for $157.97, and a sweater for $19.95 at Shoppers R Us.

How much money did she spend? _____

10. Show how she wrote a check for this amount.

Date _____

PAY TO THE
ORDER OF _____ $ [   ]

_____ DOLLARS

_____

Name _____

10's

1	2	3	4	5	6	7	8	9	10
11	12	13	14	15	16	17	18	19	20
21	22	23	24	25	26	27	28	29	30
31	32	33	34	35	36	37	38	39	40
41	42	43	44	45	46	47	48	49	50
51	52	53	54	55	56	57	58	59	60
61	62	63	64	65	66	67	68	69	70
71	72	73	74	75	76	77	78	79	80
81	82	83	84	85	86	87	88	89	90
91	92	93	94	95	96	97	98	99	100

5's

1	2	3	4	5	6	7	8	9	10
11	12	13	14	15	16	17	18	19	20
21	22	23	24	25	26	27	28	29	30
31	32	33	34	35	36	37	38	39	40
41	42	43	44	45	46	47	48	49	50
51	52	53	54	55	56	57	58	59	60
61	62	63	64	65	66	67	68	69	70
71	72	73	74	75	76	77	78	79	80
81	82	83	84	85	86	87	88	89	90
91	92	93	94	95	96	97	98	99	100

2's

1	2	3	4	5	6	7	8	9	10
11	12	13	14	15	16	17	18	19	20
21	22	23	24	25	26	27	28	29	30
31	32	33	34	35	36	37	38	39	40
41	42	43	44	45	46	47	48	49	50
51	52	53	54	55	56	57	58	59	60
61	62	63	64	65	66	67	68	69	70
71	72	73	74	75	76	77	78	79	80
81	82	83	84	85	86	87	88	89	90
91	92	93	94	95	96	97	98	99	100

4's

1	2	3	4	5	6	7	8	9	10
11	12	13	14	15	16	17	18	19	20
21	22	23	24	25	26	27	28	29	30
31	32	33	34	35	36	37	38	39	40
41	42	43	44	45	46	47	48	49	50
51	52	53	54	55	56	57	58	59	60
61	62	63	64	65	66	67	68	69	70
71	72	73	74	75	76	77	78	79	80
81	82	83	84	85	86	87	88	89	90
91	92	93	94	95	96	97	98	99	100

8's

1	2	3	4	5	6	7	8	9	10
11	12	13	14	15	16	17	18	19	20
21	22	23	24	25	26	27	28	29	30
31	32	33	34	35	36	37	38	39	40
41	42	43	44	45	46	47	48	49	50
51	52	53	54	55	56	57	58	59	60
61	62	63	64	65	66	67	68	69	70
71	72	73	74	75	76	77	78	79	80
81	82	83	84	85	86	87	88	89	90
91	92	93	94	95	96	97	98	99	100

Name _____

3's

1	2	3	4	5	6	7	8	9	10
11	12	13	14	15	16	17	18	19	20
21	22	23	24	25	26	27	28	29	30
31	32	33	34	35	36	37	38	39	40
41	42	43	44	45	46	47	48	49	50
51	52	53	54	55	56	57	58	59	60
61	62	63	64	65	66	67	68	69	70
71	72	73	74	75	76	77	78	79	80
81	82	83	84	85	86	87	88	89	90
91	92	93	94	95	96	97	98	99	100

6's

1	2	3	4	5	6	7	8	9	10
11	12	13	14	15	16	17	18	19	20
21	22	23	24	25	26	27	28	29	30
31	32	33	34	35	36	37	38	39	40
41	42	43	44	45	46	47	48	49	50
51	52	53	54	55	56	57	58	59	60
61	62	63	64	65	66	67	68	69	70
71	72	73	74	75	76	77	78	79	80
81	82	83	84	85	86	87	88	89	90
91	92	93	94	95	96	97	98	99	100

9's

1	2	3	4	5	6	7	8	9	10
11	12	13	14	15	16	17	18	19	20
21	22	23	24	25	26	27	28	29	30
31	32	33	34	35	36	37	38	39	40
41	42	43	44	45	46	47	48	49	50
51	52	53	54	55	56	57	58	59	60
61	62	63	64	65	66	67	68	69	70
71	72	73	74	75	76	77	78	79	80
81	82	83	84	85	86	87	88	89	90
91	92	93	94	95	96	97	98	99	100

7's

1	2	3	4	5	6	7	8	9	10
11	12	13	14	15	16	17	18	19	20
21	22	23	24	25	26	27	28	29	30
31	32	33	34	35	36	37	38	39	40
41	42	43	44	45	46	47	48	49	50
51	52	53	54	55	56	57	58	59	60
61	62	63	64	65	66	67	68	69	70
71	72	73	74	75	76	77	78	79	80
81	82	83	84	85	86	87	88	89	90
91	92	93	94	95	96	97	98	99	100

Name _____ Score: _____ **M-100**

6 × 1	2 × 5	7 × 0	4 × 4	1 × 2	9 × 5	3 × 3	8 × 5	0 × 4	9 × 9
1 × 5	7 × 4	3 × 2	8 × 9	0 × 3	4 × 1	9 × 3	2 × 6	4 × 8	9 × 0
5 × 2	6 × 3	0 × 7	9 × 2	4 × 7	2 × 3	6 × 9	3 × 5	9 × 1	6 × 4
7 × 7	2 × 9	6 × 5	1 × 8	9 × 4	3 × 6	7 × 9	0 × 6	8 × 1	4 × 2
4 × 9	1 × 1	5 × 0	3 × 8	7 × 5	2 × 4	6 × 6	5 × 3	1 × 0	8 × 8
4 × 3	7 × 8	2 × 1	5 × 4	6 × 6	0 × 0	3 × 7	4 × 4	8 × 6	3 × 1
2 × 7	3 × 0	9 × 9	6 × 7	1 × 3	4 × 5	8 × 3	0 × 1	3 × 3	7 × 2
3 × 9	8 × 4	0 × 2	5 × 5	7 × 6	1 × 6	5 × 5	2 × 2	6 × 8	7 × 1
8 × 2	1 × 7	9 × 8	4 × 6	8 × 0	7 × 3	0 × 9	5 × 6	6 × 2	4 × 0
0 × 8	9 × 6	3 × 4	8 × 7	2 × 0	5 × 7	6 × 0	1 × 4	8 × 8	5 × 9

3-110Fa

Name _____

Today's Problem

Coin Cup

Q	D	N	P	Total Coins
				___

Today's Date is _____

Today's Pattern _____

Today's Problem

Coin Cup

Q	D	N	P	Total Coins
				___

Today's Date is _____

Today's Pattern _____

Today's Problem

Coin Cup

Q	D	N	P	Total Coins
				___

Today's Date is _____

Today's Pattern _____

Today's Problem

Coin Cup

Q	D	N	P	Total Coins
				___

Today's Date is _____

Today's Pattern _____

Today's Problem

Coin Cup

Q	D	N	P	Total Coins
				___

Today's Date is _____

Today's Pattern _____

3-*R1Ma

Name **•**
    (Draw a 3" line segment.)

Date **•**

(Draw a line segment 1" shorter than your name line segment.)

1. The temperature on January 19th in Juneau, Alaska was 19°F. The temperature on February 19th was 26°F. How much warmer was it on February 19th? Fill in the towers to help you.

   Number sentence _____

   Answer _____

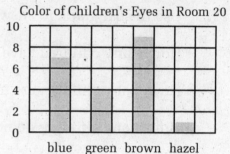

difference

larger   smaller

_____ _____

2. Use the bar graph to answer these questions.

   How many children have blue eyes? _____

   How many children are in Room 20? _____

   How many children do not have brown eyes? _____

   How many more children have brown eyes than have green eyes? _____

   Color of Children's Eyes in Room 20

   blue green brown hazel

3. Write the expanded form for each number.

   703 _____   2,405 _____

4. Find each product.

   $$\begin{array}{r} 3\,0 \\ \times\ \ 9 \\ \hline \end{array} \qquad \begin{array}{r} 9,0\,0\,0 \\ \times\ \ \ \ \ 5 \\ \hline \end{array} \qquad \begin{array}{r} 2\,0\,0 \\ \times\ \ \ 4 \\ \hline \end{array}$$

   $3 \times 7{,}000 =$ _____

   $8 \times 60 =$ _____

5. Find the area of the rectangles.

   30 cm

   8 cm

   _____ square centimeters

   9"

   40"

   _____ square inches

6. Find the answers.

   $836 − $499 $500 − $38 $1,715.63 + $109.47

Name _____

Date _____

1. The temperature in Orlando, Florida on January 20th was 68°F. On February 20th, the temperature was 76°F. How much warmer was it on February 20th? Fill in the towers to help you.

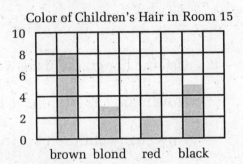

difference

larger   smaller

_____ _____

   Number sentence _____

   Answer _____

2. Use the bar graph to answer these questions.

   How many children have black hair? _____

   How many children are in Room 15? _____

   How many children do not have blond hair? _____

   How many more children have brown hair than have blond hair? _____

Color of Children's Hair in Room 15

(bar graph: brown 8, blond 3, red 2, black 5)

brown blond red black

3. Write the expanded form for each number.

   580 _____   1,056 _____

4. Find each product.

   $$\begin{array}{r} 7\,0 \\ \times\ 8 \\ \hline \end{array}\qquad \begin{array}{r} 3,0\,0\,0 \\ \times\quad 6 \\ \hline \end{array}\qquad \begin{array}{r} 9\,0\,0 \\ \times\quad 8 \\ \hline \end{array}$$

   $8 \times 4{,}000 =$ _____

   $7 \times 900 =$ _____

5. Find the area of the rectangles.

   40 cm
   6 cm

   7"
   30"

   _____ square centimeters   _____ square inches

6. Find the answers.

   $132 - $83 $400 - $209 $275.39 + $86.58

●

6 × 1	2 × 5	7 × 0	4 × 4	1 × 2	9 × 5	3 × 3	8 × 5	0 × 4	9 × 9
1 × 5	7 × 4	3 × 2	8 × 9	0 × 3	4 × 1	9 × 3	2 × 6	4 × 8	9 × 0
5 × 2	6 × 3	0 × 7	9 × 2	4 × 7	2 × 3	6 × 9	3 × 5	9 × 1	6 × 4
7 × 7	2 × 9	6 × 5	1 × 8	9 × 4	3 × 6	7 × 9	0 × 6	8 × 1	4 × 2
4 × 9	1 × 1	5 × 0	3 × 8	7 × 5	2 × 4	6 × 6	5 × 3	1 × 0	8 × 8
4 × 3	7 × 8	2 × 1	5 × 4	6 × 6	0 × 0	3 × 7	4 × 4	8 × 6	3 × 1
2 × 7	3 × 0	9 × 9	6 × 7	1 × 3	4 × 5	8 × 3	0 × 1	3 × 3	7 × 2
3 × 9	8 × 4	0 × 2	5 × 5	7 × 6	1 × 6	5 × 5	2 × 2	6 × 8	7 × 1
8 × 2	1 × 7	9 × 8	4 × 6	8 × 0	7 × 3	0 × 9	5 × 6	6 × 2	4 × 0
0 × 8	9 × 6	3 × 4	8 × 7	2 × 0	5 × 7	6 × 0	1 × 4	8 × 8	5 × 9

Name •
(Draw a $2\frac{1}{2}$" line segment.)

Date •

(Draw a line segment $\frac{1}{2}$" longer than the name line segment.)

1. John and his sister planted bean seeds. When John's
plant was 30 cm tall, his sister's plant was 22 cm tall.
How much taller was John's plant?

difference

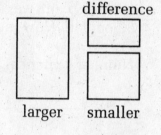

Number sentence _____

larger   smaller

Answer _____

_____   _____

2. The cost of the eraser is 73¢. How much change will you receive from $1.00?

Answer _____

3. Fill in the numbers on the number line. Where is each arrow pointing?

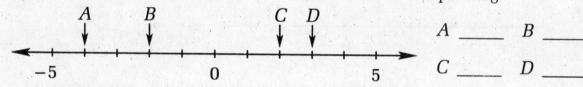

    A   B   C D

A _____   B _____

C _____   D _____

4. Manuel collects old coins. How many years old is each of these coins?

_____

_____

5. Find the products.

$8 \times 50 =$ _____ $6 \times 900 =$ _____ $4 \times 7,000 =$ _____

6. Find the amount of money in
each pocket.

Which pocket has the
least amount of money? _____

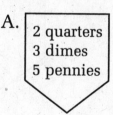

A.
| 2 quarters |
| 3 dimes |
| 5 pennies |

B.
| 3 quarters |
| 2 nickels |
| 10 pennies |

C.
| 6 dimes |
| 3 nickels |
| 15 pennies |

_____   _____   _____

7. Fill in the missing numbers.

$9 + 9 + 9 + 9 = 4 \times \boxed{}$ $\sqrt{100} + \sqrt{64} = 2 \times \boxed{}$

3-112Wa

Name _____

Date _____

1. Laura and her brother planted bean seeds. When Laura's plant was 25 cm tall, her brother's plant was 32 cm tall. How much taller was her brother's plant?

    difference

    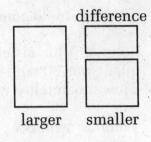

    larger   smaller

    Number sentence _____

    _____   _____

    Answer _____

2. The cost of the pencil is 68¢. How much change will you receive from $1.00?

    Answer _____

3. Fill in the numbers on the number line. Where is each arrow pointing?

    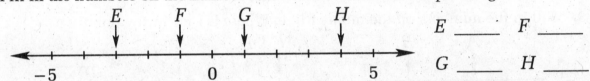

    E _____   F _____

    G _____   H _____

4. These are two more coins from Manuel's collection. How many years old is each of these coins?

     _____    _____

5. Find the products.

    $2 \times 90 =$ _____ $3 \times 6,000 =$ _____ $4 \times 400 =$ _____

6. Find the amount of money in each pocket.

    A. 1 quarter
        2 dimes
        7 nickels

    B. 7 dimes
        3 nickels
        7 pennies

    C. 2 quarters
        5 nickels
        10 pennies

    Which pocket has the least amount of money? _____

    _____   _____   _____

7. Fill in the missing numbers.

    $634 - 125 = 5 \times 100 +$ ☐ $9 \times$ ☐ $= 62 - 35$

7 − 1	10 − 4	9 − 0	16 − 9	5 − 4	12 − 6	9 − 7	11 − 3	8 − 2	6 − 6
9 − 4	6 − 3	11 − 6	10 − 2	6 − 1	12 − 8	2 − 0	9 − 3	7 − 2	6 − 5
5 − 5	11 − 4	4 − 2	15 − 9	8 − 0	10 − 6	14 − 5	9 − 9	7 − 6	12 − 7
9 − 5	17 − 9	8 − 4	13 − 8	9 − 2	11 − 5	15 − 6	5 − 1	8 − 5	16 − 8
8 − 6	11 − 7	1 − 0	7 − 3	9 − 6	4 − 3	17 − 8	10 − 5	12 − 4	13 − 7
8 − 3	16 − 7	10 − 3	4 − 1	6 − 2	13 − 5	7 − 0	14 − 9	11 − 2	10 − 8
13 − 9	10 − 7	18 − 9	14 − 6	1 − 1	12 − 3	7 − 5	4 − 1	11 − 8	7 − 7
2 − 2	12 − 5	3 − 1	15 − 7	10 − 1	6 − 0	13 − 4	5 − 2	9 − 8	3 − 0
11 − 9	7 − 6	13 − 6	3 − 3	14 − 8	9 − 1	6 − 4	12 − 9	7 − 4	8 − 7
4 − 4	15 − 8	3 − 2	5 − 0	5 − 3	8 − 8	14 − 7	10 − 9	0 − 0	8 − 1

3-113Fa

Name •
(Draw a $3\frac{3}{4}$" line segment.)

Date •

(Draw a 93 mm line segment.)

1. My sister is 8 years older than I. I'm 14 years old. How old is my sister?

   Number sentence _____

   Answer _____

2. Fourteen children voted for chocolate. Five children voted for strawberry. Ten children voted for vanilla.

   Draw a graph to show how many children voted for each flavor. (Number the graph by 2's.)

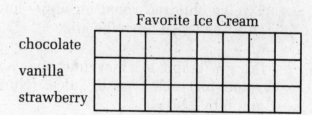

   How many children voted? _____

   What fractional part of the children chose chocolate? _____

3. Multiply.

   4×235 7×82
   $4 \times (200 + 30 + 5)$
   _____   _____

4. What is the perimeter of the rectangle? _____ inches

   What is the area of the rectangle? _____ square inches

5. Donna was born in 1953. How old will she be on her birthday this year? _____

6. Use the correct comparison symbol (>, <, or =).

   63×100 ☐ $4{,}250 + 2{,}173$ $249 - 163$ ☐ $827 - 734$

   8 weeks ☐ 54 days

1. My aunt is twenty-one years older than I. I'm twelve years old. How old is my aunt?

   difference

   Number sentence _____

   Answer _____

   larger   smaller

   _____   _____

2. Seven children voted for orange juice. Twelve children voted for apple juice. Nine children voted for grape juice.

   Favorite Juice

   apple

   orange

   grape

   Draw a graph to show how many children voted for each type of juice. (Number the graph by 2's.)

   How many children voted? _____

   What fractional part of the children chose grape juice? _____

3. Multiply.

   5×648

   $5 \times (600 + 40 + 8)$

   3×52

   _____

4. What is the perimeter of the rectangle? _____ inches

   What is the area of the rectangle? _____ square inches

   7"

   2"

5. Tania was born in 1979. How old will Tania be on her birthday this year? _____

6. Use the correct comparison symbol (>, <, or =).

   10×55 [ ] $1{,}708 + 2{,}483$ $529 - 217$ [ ] $421 - 109$

   45 days [ ] 6 weeks

Name _____

Find the missing dimension or area of each rectangle.

7"
2" [ ] square inches

5" 15 square inches

6"
[ ] 24 square inches

_____ _____ _____

4"
5" [ ] square inches

2" 12 square inches

3"
[ ] 6 square inches

_____ _____ _____

6"
3" [ ] square inches

4" 8 square inches

7" 21 square inches

_____ _____ _____

Name _____   Score: _____

6 ×1	2 ×5	7 ×0	4 ×4	1 ×2	9 ×5	3 ×3	8 ×5	0 ×4	9 ×9
1 ×5	7 ×4	3 ×2	8 ×9	0 ×3	4 ×1	9 ×3	2 ×6	4 ×8	9 ×0
5 ×2	6 ×3	0 ×7	9 ×2	4 ×7	2 ×3	6 ×9	3 ×5	9 ×1	6 ×4
7 ×7	2 ×9	6 ×5	1 ×8	9 ×4	3 ×6	7 ×9	0 ×6	8 ×1	4 ×2
4 ×9	1 ×1	5 ×0	3 ×8	7 ×5	2 ×4	6 ×6	5 ×3	1 ×0	8 ×8
4 ×3	7 ×8	2 ×1	5 ×4	6 ×6	0 ×0	3 ×7	4 ×4	8 ×6	3 ×1
2 ×7	3 ×0	9 ×9	6 ×7	1 ×3	4 ×5	8 ×3	0 ×1	3 ×3	7 ×2
3 ×9	8 ×4	0 ×2	5 ×5	7 ×6	1 ×6	5 ×5	2 ×2	6 ×8	7 ×1
8 ×2	1 ×7	9 ×8	4 ×6	8 ×0	7 ×3	0 ×9	5 ×6	6 ×2	4 ×0
0 ×8	9 ×6	3 ×4	8 ×7	2 ×0	5 ×7	6 ×0	1 ×4	8 ×8	5 ×9

Name •————————————————————————————•
(Measure this line segment using centimeters. _____ cm)

Date •
(Draw a $1\frac{3}{4}$" line segment.)

1. At 4:00 p.m. the temperature in Phoenix was 97°F. At midnight, the temperature was 23°F lower. What was the temperature at midnight?

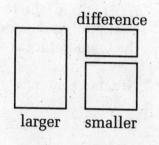

difference
larger   smaller
_____

Number sentence _____

Answer _____

2. How much change will you receive if you pay for each item with $1.00?

 24¢ _____    79¢ _____

3. Fill in the missing dimensions of the rectangles.

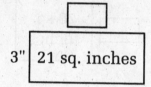

3" | 21 sq. inches

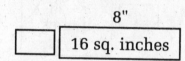

8"
16 sq. inches

4. Multiply.

   3 × 47   5 × 918
   3 × (40 + 7)
   _____   _____

5. Fill in the numbers on the number line.
   Put a point at positive two. Label it *D*.
   Put a point at negative three. Label it *R*.
   Put a point at negative two. Label it *E*.
   Put a point at positive one. Label it *A*.

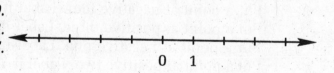

   0   1

6. Show quarter of eight on the clock.
   Write the digital time.

   ┌──────────┐
   │   :   │
   └──────────┘

7. Find the answers.

   4,692 + 428   268 − 75

Name _____   **LESSON 114B**

Date _____   *Math 3*

1. At 2:00 p.m. the temperature in Atlanta was 78°F. At 6:00 p.m. the temperature was 12°F lower. What was the temperature at 6:00 p.m.?

   Number sentence _____

   Answer _____

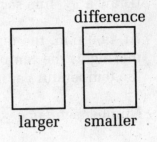

difference

larger   smaller

_____   _____

2. How much change will you receive if you pay for each item with $1.00?

 47¢ _____    81¢ _____

3. Fill in the missing dimensions of the rectangles.

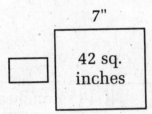

7"
| 42 sq. inches |

5"
| 20 sq. inches |

4. Multiply.

   9 × 62
   9 × (60 + 2)   _____

   2 × 807   _____

5. Fill in the numbers on the number line.
   Put a point at negative four. Label it *M*.
   Put a point at positive three. Label it *H*.
   Put a point at negative one. Label it *A*.
   Put a point at positive two. Label it *T*.

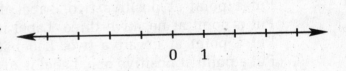

0   1

6. Show quarter of two on the clock. Write the digital time.

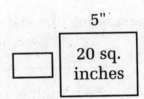

7. Find the answers.

   293 + 3,157   542 − 81

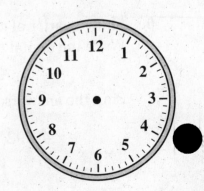

Name _____

Section 1

Today's Problem

Coin Cup				Total Coins
Q	D	N	P	
				____

Today's Date is _____

Today's Pattern _____

_____

Section 2

Today's Problem

Coin Cup				Total Coins
Q	D	N	P	
				____

Today's Date is _____

Today's Pattern _____

_____

Section 3

Today's Problem

Coin Cup				Total Coins
Q	D	N	P	
				____

Today's Date is _____

Today's Pattern _____

_____

Section 4

Today's Problem

Coin Cup				Total Coins
Q	D	N	P	
				____

Today's Date is _____

Today's Pattern _____

_____

Section 5

Today's Problem

Coin Cup				Total Coins
Q	D	N	P	
				____

Today's Date is _____

Today's Pattern _____

_____

Name •
(Draw a $3\frac{1}{2}$" line segment.)
Date •
(Draw a 9 cm line segment.)

1. Savona bought two baseballs and a glove. How much money did she spend?

   Number sentence _____

   Answer _____

SALE	
Baseball	$ 7.43
Bat	$21.79
Glove	$25.35

2. What will be the date on the last day of June, four years from now?

   _____

3. Circle all combinations of coins that equal 65¢.

   1 quarter, 4 dimes, 1 nickel   4 dimes, 4 nickels, 5 pennies

   2 quarters, 3 nickels   1 quarter, 8 nickels

4. Color the thermometer to show 16°C.

5. Show quarter of four on the clock.
   It's morning.
   Write the digital time. _____

6. Find the answers.

   $435 – $263 $2,592.35 + $691.28 $532 – $129

7. Circle the best unit of measure to use to measure each of these.

   length of a pencil:

   yards   inches   miles   pounds

   the height of the classroom door:

   millimeters   liters   feet   miles

3-115Aa

8. Fill in the missing numbers.

62 + ☐ = 100   29 + ☐ = 100

5 × 9 = ☐   100 × 9 = ☐   10 × 7 = ☐

4 × ☐ = 32   ☐ × 3 = 18   7 × ☐ = 56

9. Jeanne was born in 1948 and Beth was born in 1984. How old will Jeanne and Beth be on their birthdays this year?

Jeanne _____   Beth _____

10. Pretend you are the teacher. Circle the mistakes. Write the correct answers next to the examples with the wrong answers.

---

1. Use the correct comparison symbol (>, <, or =).

$\sqrt{64}$ + $\sqrt{9}$ | = | 170 ÷ 10 − 3   6 × 9 + 1 | > | 7 × 8

2. Write the numbers in expanded form.

<u>340 = 300 + 4</u>   <u>1,280 = 1,000 + 200 + 80</u>

3. Label the compass.

4. Find the perimeter of this rectangle.

5 cm

12 cm   1 cm

---

7 − 1	10 − 4	9 − 0	16 − 9	5 − 4	12 − 6	9 − 7	11 − 3	8 − 2	6 − 6
9 − 4	6 − 3	11 − 6	10 − 2	6 − 1	12 − 8	2 − 0	9 − 3	7 − 2	6 − 5
5 − 5	11 − 4	4 − 2	15 − 9	8 − 0	10 − 6	14 − 5	9 − 9	7 − 6	12 − 7
9 − 5	17 − 9	8 − 4	13 − 8	9 − 2	11 − 5	15 − 6	5 − 1	8 − 5	16 − 8
8 − 6	11 − 7	1 − 0	7 − 3	9 − 6	4 − 3	17 − 8	10 − 5	12 − 4	13 − 7
8 − 3	16 − 7	10 − 3	4 − 1	6 − 2	13 − 5	7 − 0	14 − 9	11 − 2	10 − 8
13 − 9	10 − 7	18 − 9	14 − 6	1 − 1	12 − 3	7 − 5	4 − 1	11 − 8	7 − 7
2 − 2	12 − 5	3 − 1	15 − 7	10 − 1	6 − 0	13 − 4	5 − 2	9 − 8	3 − 0
11 − 9	7 − 6	13 − 6	3 − 3	14 − 8	9 − 1	6 − 4	12 − 9	7 − 4	8 − 7
4 − 4	15 − 8	3 − 2	5 − 0	5 − 3	8 − 8	14 − 7	10 − 9	0 − 0	8 − 1

3-115Fa

Name _____ •
  (Draw a 3" line segment.)

Date _____ •

  (Draw a 104 mm line segment.)

1. Christine is 27 years younger than her father. Her father is 35 years old. How old is Christine?

   Number sentence _____

   Answer _____

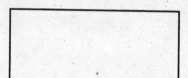

2. Draw 9 balls. Circle one third of the balls.

   $\frac{1}{3}$ of 9 = _____

3. Fill in the missing dimension of each rectangle.

   3" | 18 sq. inches

   2" | 16 sq. inches

4. Multiply.

   6 × 52
   6 × (50 + 2)
   _____

   3 × 417
   _____

5. What time is shown on the clock? Write the digital time. Write the time two ways using words.

   [:]   _____

           _____

6. Three children will share fifteen cookies. Show how they will do this.
   How many cookies will each child receive? _____
   Write a division example to show this.

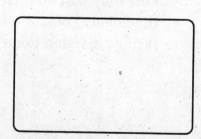

Name _____

Date _____

1. Sarah is 6 years older than her sister. Her sister is 25 years old. How old is Sarah?

   difference

   Number sentence _____

   larger   smaller

   Answer _____

   _____   _____

2. Draw 8 stars. Circle one fourth of the stars.

   $\frac{1}{4}$ of 8 = _____

3. Fill in the missing dimension of each rectangle.

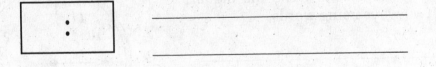

   7"

   | 21 sq. inches

   5"

   | 20 sq. in.

4. Multiply.

   5×93 7×243
   $5 \times (90 + 3)$ _____

5. What time is shown on the clock? Write the digital time. Write the time in two ways using words.

   ⬚ : ⬚   _____

   _____

6. Five children will share twenty cookies. Show how they will do this.
   How many cookies will each child receive? _____
   Write a division example to show this.

$35 \div 7 =$

$28 \div 7 =$

$0 \div 2 =$

$16 \div 2 =$

$35 \div 5 =$

$12 \div 2 =$

$0 \div 5 =$

$42 \div 7 =$

$45 \div 5 =$

$18 \div 2 =$

$21 \div 7 =$

$14 \div 7 =$

$15 \div 5 =$

$2 \div 2 =$

$20 \div 5 =$

$5 \div 5 =$

$10 \div 2 =$

$7 \div 7 =$

$49 \div 7 =$

$63 \div 7 =$

$4 \div 2 =$

$30 \div 5 =$

$14 \div 2 =$

$10 \div 5 =$

$8 \div 2 =$

Score: _____

3-116Fa

Name ●————————————————————————————————————●

(Measure this line segment using millimeters. _____ mm)

Date ●

(Draw a $2\frac{1}{4}''$ line segment.)

1. Alice, Jane, and Mary collect post cards. Jane has three more cards than Mary. If Mary has seven cards, how many cards does Jane have?

   Number sentence _____ Answer _____

   larger   smaller

   difference

   Alice has four cards less than Jane. How many cards does Alice have?

   Number sentence _____ Answer _____

   larger   smaller

   difference

2. The cost of the donut is 45¢. Mrs. Baylis paid for the donut with a one-dollar bill.

   How much change will you give her? _____

   What coins will you use to make that amount? _____

3. Write the answers.

   $\frac{16}{2}$ = _____ $5\overline{)30}$ $63 \div 7 =$ _____

4. Write a multiplication number sentence for this picture.

   Number sentence _____

   Write a division example for this picture. $\overline{)}$

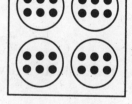

● = 1 marble

5. Fill in the numbers on the number line.
   Put a point at negative 1. Label it U.
   Put a point at positive 4. Label it E.

   C   *B*

   0 1

   Where is arrow B pointing? _____   Where is arrow C pointing? _____

6. Find the answers.

   $200 - 146$ $\$217.36 + \$37.29$

Name _____

Date _____

1. Jill, Margaret, and Karen collect old pennies. Margaret has 3 more pennies than Karen. If Karen has 6 pennies, how many pennies does Margaret have?

   Number sentence _____ Answer _____

   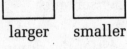
   larger   smaller   difference

   Jill has 5 more old pennies than Margaret. How many pennies does Jill have?

   Number sentence _____ Answer _____

   larger   smaller   difference

2. The cost of the bagel is 74¢. Mrs. McGinnis paid for the bagel with a one-dollar bill.

   How much change will you give her? _____

   What coins will you use to make that amount? _____

3. Write the answers.

   $28 \div 7 =$ ____ $2\overline{)14}$ $\dfrac{45}{5} =$ ____

4. Write a multiplication number sentence for this picture.

   _____

   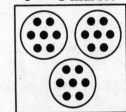
   ● = 1 marble

   Write a division example for this picture. $\overline{)}$

5. Fill in the numbers on the number line.
   Put a point at positive 3. Label it *N*.
   Put a point at negative 3. Label it *C*.

   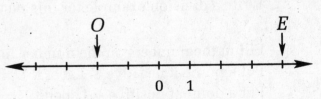

   Where is arrow *E* pointing? _____   Where is arrow *O* pointing? _____

6. Find the answers.

   $400 - 271$ $\$81.37 + \$163.21$

Name _____

1.

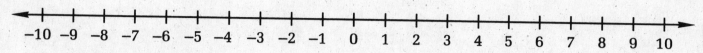

Number sentence _____

2.

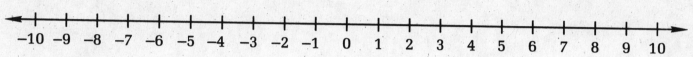

Number sentence _____

3.

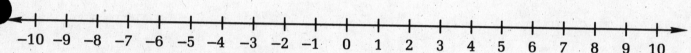

Number sentence _____

4.

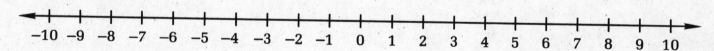

Number sentence _____

5.

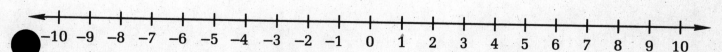

Number sentence _____

3-117Ma

$5\overline{)25}$ $2\overline{)6}$ $7\overline{)14}$ $5\overline{)20}$ $7\overline{)49}$

$2\overline{)18}$ $7\overline{)7}$ $2\overline{)4}$ $5\overline{)30}$ $7\overline{)63}$

$5\overline{)0}$ $2\overline{)8}$ $5\overline{)40}$ $7\overline{)28}$ $2\overline{)2}$

$5\overline{)35}$ $7\overline{)21}$ $2\overline{)0}$ $5\overline{)45}$ $2\overline{)14}$

$7\overline{)0}$ $5\overline{)10}$ $7\overline{)42}$ $2\overline{)12}$ $7\overline{)35}$

Score: _____

3-117Fa

6 × 1	2 × 5	7 × 0	4 × 4	1 × 2	9 × 5	3 × 3	8 × 5	0 × 4	9 × 9
1 × 5	7 × 4	3 × 2	8 × 9	0 × 3	4 × 1	9 × 3	2 × 6	4 × 8	9 × 0
5 × 2	6 × 3	0 × 7	9 × 2	4 × 7	2 × 3	6 × 9	3 × 5	9 × 1	6 × 4
7 × 7	2 × 9	6 × 5	1 × 8	9 × 4	3 × 6	7 × 9	0 × 6	8 × 1	4 × 2
4 × 9	1 × 1	5 × 0	3 × 8	7 × 5	2 × 4	6 × 6	5 × 3	1 × 0	8 × 8
4 × 3	7 × 8	2 × 1	5 × 4	6 × 6	0 × 0	3 × 7	4 × 4	8 × 6	3 × 1
2 × 7	3 × 0	9 × 9	6 × 7	1 × 3	4 × 5	8 × 3	0 × 1	3 × 3	7 × 2
3 × 9	8 × 4	0 × 2	5 × 5	7 × 6	1 × 6	5 × 5	2 × 2	6 × 8	7 × 1
8 × 2	1 × 7	9 × 8	4 × 6	8 × 0	7 × 3	0 × 9	5 × 6	6 × 2	4 × 0
0 × 8	9 × 6	3 × 4	8 × 7	2 × 0	5 × 7	6 × 0	1 × 4	8 × 8	5 × 9

3-117Fb

Name _____ •
 (Draw a 12 cm 8 mm line segment.)

Date _____ •

(Draw a congruent line segment. Measure it using millimeters. _____ mm)

1. Amber has 83¢. Erica has 15¢ less than Amber. How much money does Erica have? Fill in the towers to help you.

    Number sentence _____

    Answer _____

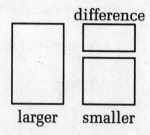

difference

larger   smaller

_____ _____

2. Jason drew number lines to show what happened in two stories. Write number sentences to match the number lines.

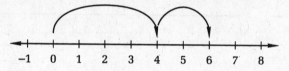   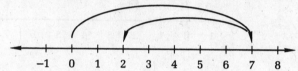

    _____   _____

3. Measure the sides of this rectangle using centimeters.

    What is the perimeter? _____ centimeters

    What is the area? _____ square centimeters

4. How much money is this? _____

Q	D	N	P
2	1	3	2

5. What was the date 4 days ago? _____

    What day of the week will it be 15 days from today? _____

6. Find the answers.

    4 × 2,039   7 0 2 $4, 8 9 6.8 3
    4 × (2,000 + 30 + 9)   − 6 2 1   + 2, 1 0 4.1 6
    _____   _____   _____

Name _____

Date _____

1. Flora has 74¢. Simone has 13¢ less than Flora. How much
   money does Simone have? Fill in the towers to help you.

   Number sentence _____

   Answer _____

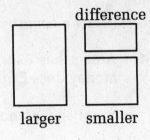

difference

larger   smaller

_____ _____

2. Andrew drew number lines to show what happened in two stories. Write number
   sentences to match the number lines.

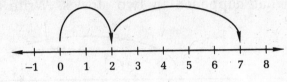 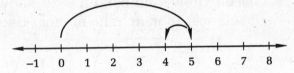

   _____   _____

3. What is the perimeter of this rectangle? _____ inches

   What is the area of this rectangle? _____ square inches

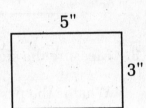

5"

3"

4. How much money is this? _____

Q	D	N	P
1	4	2	3

5. What was the date 5 days ago? _____

   What day of the week will it be 21 days from today? _____

6. Find the answers.

   3 × 6,104
   3 × (6,000 + 100 + 4)

   $\begin{array}{r} 5\ 1\ 0 \\ -\ 3\ 0\ 1 \\ \hline \end{array}$

   $\begin{array}{r} \$2,\ 8\ 7\ 9.6\ 3 \\ +\ 4,\ 1\ 2\ 1.2\ 1 \\ \hline \end{array}$

Name _____

PARALLEL LINE SEGMENTS

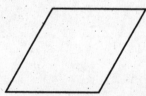

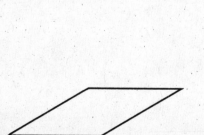
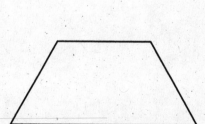
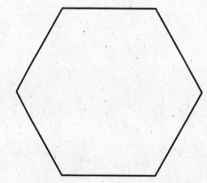

3-118Ma

$$\frac{12}{2} = \qquad \frac{10}{5} = \qquad \frac{21}{7} = \qquad \frac{30}{5} = \qquad \frac{8}{2} =$$

$$\frac{0}{7} = \qquad \frac{40}{5} = \qquad \frac{16}{2} = \qquad \frac{7}{7} = \qquad \frac{63}{7} =$$

$$\frac{35}{5} = \qquad \frac{4}{2} = \qquad \frac{42}{7} = \qquad \frac{20}{5} = \qquad \frac{0}{2} =$$

$$\frac{56}{7} = \qquad \frac{15}{5} = \qquad \frac{28}{7} = \qquad \frac{10}{2} = \qquad \frac{45}{5} =$$

$$\frac{2}{2} = \qquad \frac{49}{7} = \qquad \frac{0}{5} = \qquad \frac{14}{7} = \qquad \frac{18}{2} =$$

$$\frac{5}{5} = \qquad \frac{14}{2} = \qquad \frac{35}{7} = \qquad \frac{6}{2} = \qquad \frac{25}{5} =$$

Name _____●_____
(Draw a $3\frac{1}{2}$" line segment.)

Date _____●_____

(Draw a 102 mm line segment. It is about _____ inches long.)

1. LaToya is 47 years younger than her grandmother. Her grandmother is 56 years old. How old is LaToya? Fill in the towers to help you.

   Number sentence _____

   Answer _____

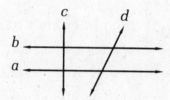

larger   smaller
_____   _____

2. Show 6 − 2 = 4 on the number line.

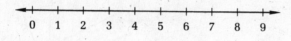

0   1   2   3   4   5   6   7   8   9

3. Which lines are parallel? _____ and _____

4. Bert had $340.25. He spent $196.75 for a new bicycle.

   How much money does he have left? _____

   Show how he wrote $196.75 on a check.

   _____ DOLLARS

5. These are cheesecakes. Divide the first cheesecake into halves. Divide the second cheesecake into thirds. Divide the third cheesecake into fourths. Each cheesecake will have 12 strawberries. () $\frac{1}{2}$ of 12 = _____ $\frac{1}{3}$ of 12 = _____ $\frac{1}{4}$ of 12 = _____

   Draw the strawberries on the cheesecake so that each piece has the same amount.

6. Find the products.

   8 × 400   3 × 5,000   6 × 90

Name _____

Date _____

1. Theresa is 15 years old. Her sister, Marie, is 9 years younger. How old is Marie? Fill in the towers to help you.

   Number sentence _____

   Answer _____

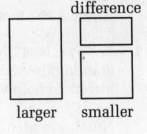

2. Show 1 + 3 = 4 on the number line.

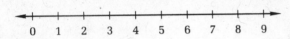

3. Which lines are parallel? _____ and _____

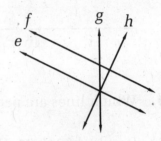

4. Jenelle had $352.60. She spent $83.23 for school clothes.

   How much money does she have left? _____

   Show how she wrote $83.23 on a check.

   _____ DOLLARS

5. These are cheesecakes. Divide the first cheesecake into halves. Divide the second cheesecake into fourths. Divide the third cheesecake into eighths. Each cheesecake will have 8 strawberries. (🍓)

 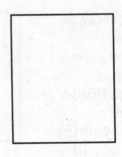 

   $\frac{1}{2}$ of 8 = _____ $\frac{1}{4}$ of 8 = _____ $\frac{1}{8}$ of 8 = _____

   Draw the strawberries on the cheesecake so that each piece has the same amount.

6. Find the products.

   $7 \times 8{,}000$ $9 \times 5{,}000$ 8×90

Name _____

Today's Problem

Coin Cup

Q	D	N	P	Total Coins

Today's Date is _____

Today's Pattern _____

_____

Today's Problem

Coin Cup

Q	D	N	P	Total Coins

Today's Date is _____

Today's Pattern _____

_____

Today's Problem

Coin Cup

Q	D	N	P	Total Coins

Today's Date is _____

Today's Pattern _____

_____

Today's Problem

Coin Cup

Q	D	N	P	Total Coins

Today's Date is _____

Today's Pattern _____

_____

Today's Problem

Coin Cup

Q	D	N	P	Total Coins

Today's Date is _____

Today's Pattern _____

_____

35 ÷ 7 =

12 ÷ 2 =

21 ÷ 7 =

5 ÷ 5 =

4 ÷ 2 =

28 ÷ 7 =

0 ÷ 5 =

14 ÷ 7 =

10 ÷ 2 =

30 ÷ 5 =

0 ÷ 2 =

42 ÷ 7 =

15 ÷ 5 =

7 ÷ 7 =

14 ÷ 2 =

16 ÷ 2 =

45 ÷ 5 =

2 ÷ 2 =

49 ÷ 7 =

10 ÷ 5 =

35 ÷ 5 =

18 ÷ 2 =

20 ÷ 5 =

63 ÷ 7 =

8 ÷ 2 =

Score: _____

Name ●━━━━━━━━━━━━━━━━━●

(Measure this line segment using millimeters. _____ mm)

LESSON 119A

Math 3

Date ●━━━━━━━━━━━●

(Measure this line segment using inches. _____")

1. Katie's birthday is on July 6th. How many more days is it until Katie's birthday?

   Answer _____

2. The cost of the ruler is 58¢. You give the clerk $1.00.

   How much change will you receive? _____

   What coins will you get? _____

3. Use these digit cards to write the following three-digit numbers.

   a three-digit odd number _____

   the largest three-digit number _____

4. Trace the parallel line segments using a red crayon.

   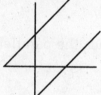

5. Fill in the missing numbers and write the rule.

T	1	2	3	5	7	10	30	T
V	5	6	7					

6. Tasha was born in 1962. How old will she be on this year's birthday? _____

7. Find the answers.

   4×629
   $4 \times (600 + 20 + 9)$

   $18 \div 2$

   $\dfrac{35}{5}$

   $7\overline{)56}$ $2\overline{)12}$ $600 - 243 $879.21 + 39.53

1. Allison's birthday is on August 2nd. How many more days is it until Allison's birthday?

    Answer _____

2. The cost of the pen is 73¢. You give the clerk $1.00.

    How much change will you receive? _____

    What coins will you get? _____

3. Use these digit cards to write the following three-digit numbers.

    a three-digit even number _____

    the smallest three-digit number _____

4. Trace the parallel line segments using a red crayon.

5. Fill in the missing numbers and write the rule.

W	1	2	3	5	7	10	30	W
X	0	1	2					

6. Melinda was born in 1971. How old will she be on this year's birthday? _____

7. Find the answers.

    4×629
    $4 \times (600 + 20 + 9)$

    $40 \div 5$

    $\dfrac{21}{7}$

    $7\overline{)49}$ $2\overline{)14}$ $\$500 - \$327$ $\$482.16 + \$39.57$

Name .
(Draw a $4\frac{1}{4}$" line segment.)
Date .
(Draw an 85 mm line segment.)

1. Pretend that you have $85.75 in your checking account. Write a check to your mother for $29.50.

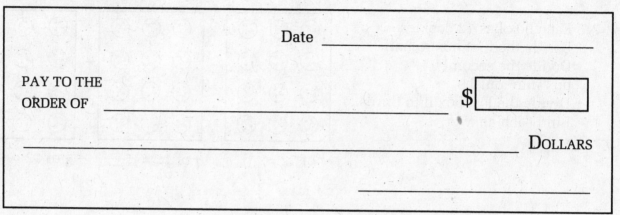

2. How much money do you have left in your checking account? _____

3. What is the area of each rectangle?

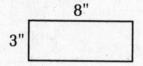
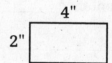

Area = _____ square inches   Area = _____ square inches

4. Sarah reads nine pages each night. How many pages will she read in one week?

Number sentence _____ Answer _____

5. What time is shown on the clocks? Write the digital time.

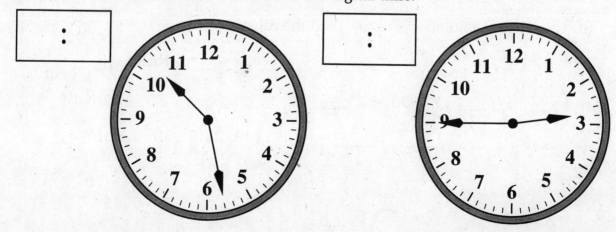

6. Find each product.

$$\begin{array}{r} 6\,0 \\ \times\ 4 \\ \hline \end{array} \qquad \begin{array}{r} 5{,}0\,0\,0 \\ \times\ 9 \\ \hline \end{array} \qquad \begin{array}{r} 6\,0\,0 \\ \times\ 7 \\ \hline \end{array} \qquad 8 \times 3{,}000 \qquad 5 \times 800$$

7. Each box has 12 cookies.
Divide the first box in half.
Divide the second
box into fourths.
Divide the last box into thirds.
Find each answer.

$\frac{1}{2}$ of 12 = _____ $\frac{1}{4}$ of 12 = _____ $\frac{1}{3}$ of 12 = _____

8. The temperature in Coal City, Illinois on March 21st was 8°C. It was 7° warmer in Luling, Texas. What was the temperature in Luling on March 21st?

Number sentence _____

Answer _____

difference

larger   smaller

_____   _____

9. Find the answers.

$$\begin{array}{r} 6\,0\,4 \\ -3\,5\,2 \\ \hline \end{array} \qquad \begin{array}{r} 5\,0\,0 \\ -1\,4\,3 \\ \hline \end{array} \qquad 230 - 114 \qquad \$426.37 + \$69.90$$

10. Complete the number patterns. Find the rules.

$\frac{1}{4}$, $\frac{2}{4}$, $\frac{3}{4}$, _____, _____, _____, _____, _____   Rule: _____

_____, _____, 27, 36, 45, _____, _____, _____, _____   Rule: _____

_____, _____, _____, _____, _____, 330, 340, 350   Rule: _____

Name _____

	1	2	3	4	5	6	7	8	9	10
Factors										

	11	12	13	14	15	16	17	18	19	20
Factors										

3-120Ma

Name _____   Score: _____   **D 13.2**

$$\frac{12}{2} =$$ $$\frac{10}{5} =$$ $$\frac{21}{7} =$$ $$\frac{30}{5} =$$ $$\frac{8}{2} =$$

$$\frac{0}{7} =$$ $$\frac{40}{5} =$$ $$\frac{16}{2} =$$ $$\frac{7}{7} =$$ $$\frac{63}{7} =$$

$$\frac{35}{5} =$$ $$\frac{4}{2} =$$ $$\frac{42}{7} =$$ $$\frac{20}{5} =$$ $$\frac{0}{2} =$$

$$\frac{56}{7} =$$ $$\frac{15}{5} =$$ $$\frac{28}{7} =$$ $$\frac{10}{2} =$$ $$\frac{45}{5} =$$

$$\frac{2}{2} =$$ $$\frac{49}{7} =$$ $$\frac{0}{5} =$$ $$\frac{14}{7} =$$ $$\frac{18}{2} =$$

$$\frac{5}{5} =$$ $$\frac{14}{2} =$$ $$\frac{35}{7} =$$ $$\frac{6}{2} =$$ $$\frac{25}{5} =$$

$5\overline{)25}$ $\quad$ $2\overline{)6}$ $\quad$ $7\overline{)14}$ $\quad$ $5\overline{)20}$ $\quad$ $7\overline{)49}$

$2\overline{)18}$ $\quad$ $7\overline{)7}$ $\quad$ $2\overline{)4}$ $\quad$ $5\overline{)30}$ $\quad$ $7\overline{)63}$

$5\overline{)0}$ $\quad$ $2\overline{)8}$ $\quad$ $5\overline{)40}$ $\quad$ $7\overline{)28}$ $\quad$ $2\overline{)2}$

$5\overline{)35}$ $\quad$ $7\overline{)21}$ $\quad$ $2\overline{)0}$ $\quad$ $5\overline{)45}$ $\quad$ $2\overline{)14}$

$7\overline{)0}$ $\quad$ $5\overline{)10}$ $\quad$ $7\overline{)42}$ $\quad$ $2\overline{)12}$ $\quad$ $7\overline{)35}$

Score: _____

Name _____•   **LESSON 121A**
(Measure this line segment using millimeters. _____ mm)   *Math 3*

Date •_____•
(Measure this line segment using inches. _____")

1. Three hundred eleven children said yes on Monday. One hundred twenty-five children said no. How many more children said yes than said no?

    What type of story is this? _____

    Number sentence _____ Answer _____

2. What time is shown on the clock?
    Write the digital time.
    Write the time using words.

    _____

    [clock box showing :]

3. Circle the word in which $\frac{4}{7}$ of the letters are vowels.

    Nevada   Delaware   Florida   Georgia   Ohio

4. Fill in the missing numbers and write the rule.

C	1	2	4	9	12	20	C
D	2	4	8		24		

5. List all the factors of each number. Circle the prime numbers. (Prime numbers have exactly two factors.)

          6   14   1

    _____   _____   _____

6. Find the answers.

        $504 − $123   63   419   5 × 207
                               × 7   ×   6

Name _____ **LESSON 121B**

Date _____ **Math 3**

1. Two hundred eighty-one children said yes on Tuesday. One hundred fifty-five children said no. How many more children said yes than said no?

   What type of story is this? _____

   Number sentence _____ Answer _____

2. What time is shown on the clock?
   Write the digital time.
   Write the time using words.

   _____

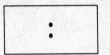

3. Circle the word in which $\frac{3}{8}$ of the letters are vowels.

   Colorado   Vermont   Montana   Michigan   Maine

4. Fill in the missing numbers and write the rule.

A	1	2	4	9	12	20	A
B	3	6	12		36		

5. List all the factors of each number. Circle the prime numbers. (Prime numbers have exactly two factors.)

   3   8   11

   _____   _____   _____

6. Find the answers.

   $300 − $142   94   304   3 × 109
                     × 8   × 9

Name _____

D 16.0

$16 \div 4 =$

$48 \div 8 =$

$24 \div 8 =$

$40 \div 8 =$

$12 \div 4 =$

$32 \div 8 =$

$12 \div 4 =$

$20 \div 4 =$

$4 \div 4 =$

$0 \div 4 =$

$0 \div 4 =$

$72 \div 8 =$

$28 \div 4 =$

$56 \div 8 =$

$72 \div 8 =$

$8 \div 4 =$

$16 \div 8 =$

$8 \div 8 =$

$0 \div 8 =$

$28 \div 4 =$

$40 \div 8 =$

$36 \div 4 =$

$64 \div 8 =$

$24 \div 4 =$

$16 \div 4 =$

Score: _____

3-122Fa

Name _____

(Measure this line segment using centimeters. _____ cm)

Date •————————————————————————————•

(Measure this line segment using millimeters. _____ mm)

1. Taylor gives his dog 3 dog biscuits a day. How many dog biscuits will the dog eat during the month of May?

   What type of story is this? _____

   Number sentence _____   Answer _____

2. Measure each side of this shape using millimeters.

   What is the perimeter? _____

   Trace the parallel line segments using a red crayon.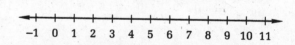

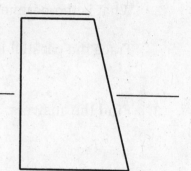

3. Find the answers.

   7 × 174 =   489
   7 × (100 + 70 + 4)   × 3

4. Show these number sentences on the number lines.

   4 + 2 = 6   7 − 5 = 2

   ┼┼┼┼┼┼┼┼┼┼┼┼┼→   ┼┼┼┼┼┼┼┼┼┼┼┼┼→
   −1 0 1 2 3 4 5 6 7 8 9 10 11   −1 0 1 2 3 4 5 6 7 8 9 10 11

5. Mrs. Gilcrist bought a dozen donuts. Five were chocolate, four were jelly, and the rest were cinnamon. Draw the donuts.

   What fractional part of the donuts is:

   chocolate? _____   jelly? _____   cinnamon? _____

6. Use the correct comparison symbol (>, <, or =).

   30 ÷ 5 ☐ $\frac{42}{7}$ $\frac{24}{8}$ ☐ 16 ÷ 4   18 ÷ 2 ☐ $\frac{28}{4}$

   207 − 129 ☐ 300 − 216   48 + 293 ☐ 307 + 36

Name _____

Date _____

1. Harvey walks his dog twice a day. How many times will he walk his dog during the month of June?

   What type of story is this? _____

   Number sentence _____   Answer _____

2. What is the perimeter of this trapezoid? _____

   Trace the parallel line segments using a crayon.

   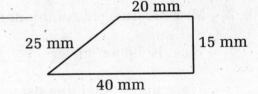

3. Find the answers.

   $$8 \times 245$$

   $$\begin{array}{r} 497 \\ \times\ \ 6 \\ \hline \end{array}$$

4. Show these number sentences on the number lines.

   $$2 + 4 = 6$$ $$7 - 2 = 5$$

   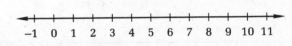

5. Mr. Fierro bought a dozen donuts. Six were jelly donuts, two were chocolate, and the rest were cinnamon.
   Draw the donuts.

   What fractional part of the donuts is:

   jelly? _____   chocolate? _____   cinnamon? _____

6. Use the correct comparison symbol (>, <, or =).

   $$56 \div 8 \ \square\ \frac{24}{4} \qquad 30 \div 5 \ \square\ \frac{14}{2} \qquad \frac{16}{8} \ \square\ 14 \div 7$$

   $$302 - 147 \ \square\ 400 - 253 \qquad\qquad 427 + 39 \ \square\ 274 + 187$$

Name _____

Today's Date is _____

Today's Pattern _____

_____

Coin Cup

Q	D	N	P	Total Coins

Today's Problem

_____

Today's Date is _____

Today's Pattern _____

_____

Coin Cup

Q	D	N	P	Total Coins

Today's Problem

_____

Today's Date is _____

Today's Pattern _____

_____

Coin Cup

Q	D	N	P	Total Coins

Today's Problem

_____

Today's Date is _____

Today's Pattern _____

_____

Coin Cup

Q	D	N	P	Total Coins

Today's Problem

_____

Today's Date is _____

Today's Pattern _____

_____

Coin Cup

Q	D	N	P	Total Coins

Today's Problem

_____

3-*R1Ma

Name _____

PERPENDICULAR LINE SEGMENTS

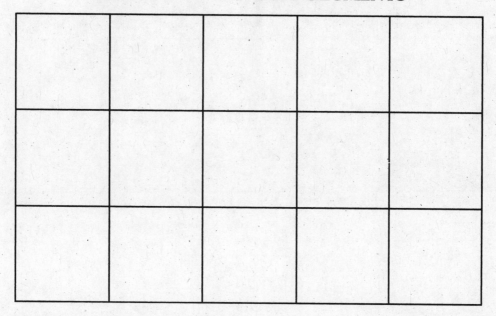

PARALLEL   PERPENDICULAR

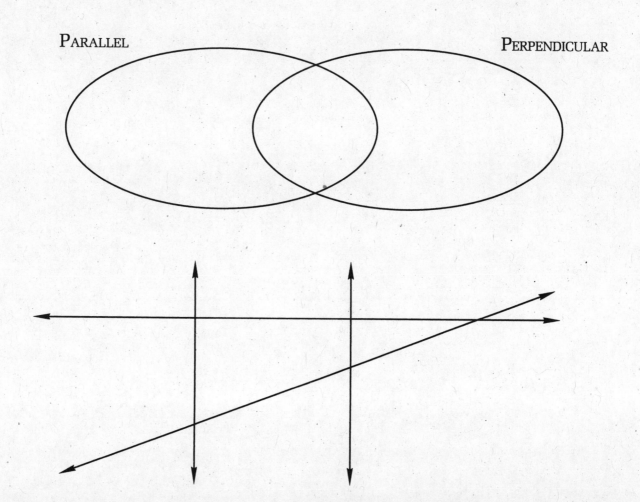

$4\overline{)24}$ $8\overline{)8}$ $4\overline{)16}$ $8\overline{)40}$ $8\overline{)72}$

$4\overline{)4}$ $8\overline{)32}$ $4\overline{)0}$ $4\overline{)20}$ $8\overline{)16}$

$8\overline{)24}$ $8\overline{)48}$ $4\overline{)28}$ $4\overline{)8}$ $8\overline{)0}$

$4\overline{)12}$ $8\overline{)56}$ $4\overline{)32}$ $8\overline{)40}$ $4\overline{)12}$

$8\overline{)24}$ $8\overline{)16}$ $8\overline{)72}$ $4\overline{)28}$ $4\overline{)4}$

Score: _____

Name _____ •

(Measure this line segment using inches. _____")

• Date •

(Draw a 7 cm 8 mm line segment.)

1. The children in Room 6 scored 8 points less than the children in Room 10. If the children in Room 10 scored 12 points, how many points did the children in Room 6 score?

   difference

   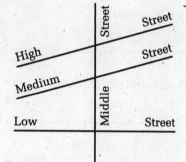

   larger   smaller

   _____ _____

   Number sentence _____

   Answer _____

2. Which streets are parallel?

   _____

   Which streets are perpendicular?

   _____

3. Use the correct comparison symbol (>, <, or =).

   $\sqrt{9} \times 400$ ☐ 2×600 $38 - 19$ ☐ $57 - 39$

   $529 + 437$ ☐ $915 + 48$ 7×126 ☐ 4×219

4. Fill in the missing dimensions of each rectangle.

   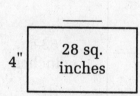

   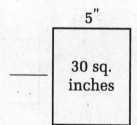

5. The cost of the eraser is 18¢. You give the clerk $1.00.

   How much change will you receive? _____

   What coins will you get? _____

6. Finish the patterns. Write the rules.

   670, 620, 570, 520, _____ , _____ , _____ , _____ , _____   Rule: _____

   _____ , _____ , _____ , $8\frac{1}{2}$, 8, $7\frac{1}{2}$, _____ , _____ , _____   Rule: _____

Name _____

Date _____

1. The children in Room 2 scored 7 points less than the children in Room 8. If the children in Room 8 scored 9 points, how many points did the children in Room 2 score?

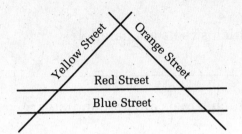

   difference

   larger   smaller

   _____ _____

   Number sentence _____

   Answer _____

2. Which streets are parallel?

   _____

   Which streets are perpendicular?

   _____

   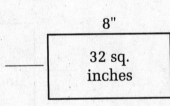

3. Use the correct comparison symbol (>, <, or =).

   $\sqrt{16} \times 300$ ☐ 3×400 $47 - 29$ ☐ $63 - 51$

   $489 + 312$ ☐ $737 + 75$ 5×148 ☐ 3×243

4. Fill in the missing dimensions of each rectangle.

   8"

   _____ | 32 sq. inches

   9"

   _____ | 63 sq. inches

5. The cost of the eraser is 83¢. You give the clerk $1.00.

   How much change will you receive? _____

   What coins will you get? _____

6. Finish the patterns. Write the rules.

   225, 250, 275, _____ , _____ , _____ , _____ , _____   Rule: _____

   _____ , _____ , _____ , $5\frac{1}{2}$, 6, $6\frac{1}{2}$, _____ , _____ , _____   Rule: _____

Name _____   Score: _____   **D 16.2**

● $\dfrac{20}{4} =$ $\dfrac{64}{8} =$ $\dfrac{4}{4} =$ $\dfrac{0}{8} =$ $\dfrac{24}{4} =$

$\dfrac{40}{8} =$ $\dfrac{8}{4} =$ $\dfrac{32}{8} =$ $\dfrac{36}{4} =$ $\dfrac{8}{8} =$

● $\dfrac{0}{4} =$ $\dfrac{28}{4} =$ $\dfrac{16}{8} =$ $\dfrac{56}{8} =$ $\dfrac{32}{4} =$

$\dfrac{24}{8} =$ $\dfrac{16}{4} =$ $\dfrac{20}{4} =$ $\dfrac{48}{8} =$ $\dfrac{0}{8} =$

● $\dfrac{36}{4} =$ $\dfrac{64}{8} =$ $\dfrac{0}{4} =$ $\dfrac{24}{4} =$ $\dfrac{8}{8} =$

3-124Fa

Name _____

(Measure this line segment using inches. _____ ")

Date _____

(Measure this line segment using millimeters. _____ mm)

1. Angelo saved forty-three dollars and twelve cents. He spent nine dollars and fifty cents for a gift for his father. How much money does he have left?

   What type of story is this? _____

   Number sentence _____ Answer _____

2. Circle the prime numbers.

   1   2   3   4   5   6   7   8   9   10

   11   12   13   14   15   16   17   18   19   20

3. What will be the date 6 months from today? _____

   What day of the week was it 8 days ago? _____

4. Write a number sentence for this picture.

   _____

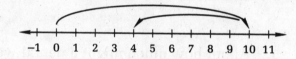

5. About how much might a book weigh?

   1 ounce   1 pound   1 centimeter   1 ton

6. I bought a post card for 35¢. How much change will I receive from a dollar? _____

7. Find the answers.

   8 × 36 $640 − $57   24 ÷ 4   56 ÷ 8

   1,207 $\frac{45}{5}$ $\frac{12}{4}$ 7)21   8)72
   ×   9

Name _____   **LESSON 124B**
                                               Math 3
Date _____

1. Philip saved fifty-two dollars and thirty cents. He spent eight dollars and seventy cents for a gift for his father. How much money does he have left?

    What type of story is this? _____

    Number sentence _____   Answer _____

2. List the prime numbers less than 20.

    _____

3. What was the date 3 months ago from today? _____

    What day of the week will it be 8 days from today? _____

4. Write a number sentence for this picture.

    _____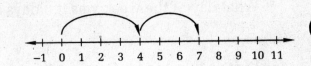

5. About how much might a pencil weigh?

        1 ounce   1 pound   1 centimeter   1 ton

6. I bought a stamp for 19¢. How much change will I receive from a dollar? _____

    What coins might that be? _____

7. Find the answers.

    7 × 46 $320 − $75   28 ÷ 7   4 ÷ 4

    2,904 $\frac{48}{8}$ $\frac{25}{5}$ 4)‾36‾   8)‾48‾
    ×   6

Name •

(Draw a $4\frac{1}{2}$" line segment.)

Date •

(Draw a 10 cm 4 mm line segment.)

1. Eddie is 63" tall. Randy is 48" tall. How much taller than Randy is Eddie?

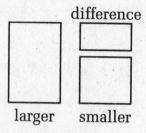

difference

larger   smaller

Number sentence _____

Answer _____

2. I spent 29¢ for a stamp to mail a letter.

How much change will I receive from a dollar? _____

What coins could I get? _____

3. Fill in the numbers on the number line.
Put a point at positive 3. Label it Y.
Put a point at negative 2. Label it X.

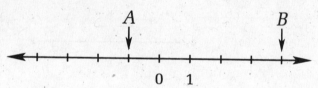

Where is arrow A pointing? _____   Where is arrow B pointing? _____

4. Find the missing dimensions of each rectangle.

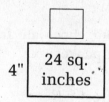

4"   24 sq. inches

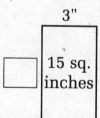

3"

15 sq. inches

5. Use the correct comparison symbol (>, <, or =).

100 × 27 ☐ 1,392 + 1,309   624 − 572 ☐ 45 + $\sqrt{49}$

35 days ☐ 6 weeks

3-125Aa

6. What was the date a week ago? _____

What day of the week will it be 6 days from today? _____

What will be the date two months from today? _____

7. Use these digit cards to write the following three-digit numbers.

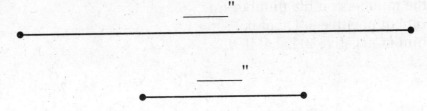

a three-digit odd number _____   a three-digit even number _____

the largest three-digit number _____   the smallest three-digit number _____

8. Measure these line segments using inches.

_____"

_____"

9. Find the answers.

$2 \times 83 =$ $7 \times 304 =$
$\underline{2 \times (80 + 3)}$ $\underline{7 \times (300 + 4)}$

10. Mrs. McDonough frosted a dozen cupcakes. She put chocolate frosting on 8 of the cupcakes and white frosting on the rest. Draw the cupcakes.

What fractional part of the cupcakes has chocolate frosting? _____

Name ______________________________

MASTER 3-125
Math 3

$\begin{array}{r}0\\3\overline{)}\end{array}$	$3\overline{)15}$	$6\overline{)0}$	$\begin{array}{r}5\\6\overline{)}\end{array}$	$\begin{array}{r}0\\9\overline{)}\end{array}$	$9\overline{)45}$
$\begin{array}{r}1\\3\overline{)}\end{array}$	$3\overline{)18}$	$6\overline{)6}$	$\begin{array}{r}6\\6\overline{)}\end{array}$	$9\overline{)9}$	$\begin{array}{r}6\\9\overline{)}\end{array}$
$\begin{array}{r}2\\3\overline{)}\end{array}$	$3\overline{)21}$	$6\overline{)12}$	$\begin{array}{r}7\\6\overline{)}\end{array}$	$\begin{array}{r}2\\9\overline{)}\end{array}$	$9\overline{)63}$
$\begin{array}{r}3\\3\overline{)}\end{array}$	$3\overline{)24}$	$6\overline{)18}$	$\begin{array}{r}8\\6\overline{)}\end{array}$	$9\overline{)27}$	$\begin{array}{r}8\\9\overline{)}\end{array}$
$\begin{array}{r}4\\3\overline{)}\end{array}$	$3\overline{)27}$	$6\overline{)24}$	$\begin{array}{r}9\\6\overline{)}\end{array}$	$\begin{array}{r}4\\9\overline{)}\end{array}$	$9\overline{)81}$

1. Write $6\overline{)42}$ in two other ways.		
2. Write $9\overline{)54}$ in two other ways.		
3. Write $\frac{24}{3}$ in two other ways.		
4. Write $\frac{18}{6}$ in two other ways.		
5. Write $63 \div 9$ in two other ways.		
6. Write $15 \div 3$ in two other ways.		

$9 \div 3 =$	$72 \div 9 =$	$27 \div 9 =$	$21 \div 3 =$	$54 \div 9 =$
$6 \div 6 =$	$24 \div 3 =$	$0 \div 3 =$	$48 \div 6 =$	$6 \div 3 =$
$18 \div 9 =$	$30 \div 6 =$	$18 \div 6 =$	$63 \div 9 =$	$24 \div 6 =$
$36 \div 6 =$	$12 \div 3 =$	$9 \div 9 =$	$0 \div 6 =$	$18 \div 3 =$
$15 \div 3 =$	$45 \div 9 =$	$54 \div 6 =$	$3 \div 3 =$	$81 \div 9 =$

Score: _____

3-125Fa

Name ●————————————————————————● **LESSON 125A**
(Measure this line segment using centimeters. _____ cm)   *Math 3*

Date ●————————————————————————●
(Measure this line segment using inches. _____ ")

1. Last year Janise weighed 68 pounds. This year she weighs 75 pounds. How much weight did she gain?

   Number sentence _____

   Answer _____

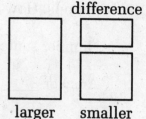
   difference
   larger   smaller
   _____ _____

2. What is the area and perimeter of each rectangle?

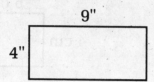
   9"
   4"

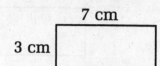
   7 cm
   3 cm

   Area = _____ square inches   Area = _____ square centimeters

   Perimeter = _____ inches   Perimeter = _____ centimeters

3. Fill in the missing numbers.

   $\boxed{} \div 6 = \sqrt{4}$ $4 \times 9 - \boxed{} = 300 \div 10$

   $72 \div 9 + \boxed{} = 12 - \sqrt{1}$

4. Fill in the missing numbers and write the rule.

E	6	2	9	13	20	53	E
F	4	0		11			

5. About how much do you weigh? _____

6. What are the smudged digits?

   200 + 3●6 = 596   5 × ●0 = 150   63 + 25 = 25 + 6●

   ___   ___   ___

   3 + 6 + 2 + 9 + 5 + 6 + 9 + 4 + 3 + 1 = 30 + 1●

   ___

Name _____

Date _____

1. Last year Jane weighed 53 pounds. This year she weighs 62 pounds. How much weight did she gain?

   Number sentence _____

   Answer _____

   difference

   larger   smaller

   _____   _____

2. What is the area and perimeter of each rectangle?

   8"

   3"

   6 cm

   4 cm

   Area = _____ square inches

   Perimeter = _____ inches

   Area = _____ square centimeters

   Perimeter = _____ centimeters

3. Fill in the missing numbers.

   $\square \div 3 = \sqrt{36}$

   $7 \times 9 - \square = 600 \div 10$

   $54 \div 6 + 2 = 12 - \square$

4. Fill in the missing numbers and write the rule.

G	6	2	9	13	20	53	G
H	13	9	16				

5. About how much did you weigh when you were born? _____
   (Ask a parent.)
   How much weight have you gained since you were born? _____

6. What are the smudged digits?

   $\blacksquare 73 + 600 = 873$ $6 \times \blacksquare 0 = 120$ $73 + 2\blacksquare = 24 + 73$

   _____   _____   _____

$3\overline{)6}$ $\quad$ $9\overline{)81}$ $\quad$ $6\overline{)30}$ $\quad$ $6\overline{)0}$ $\quad$ $3\overline{)27}$

$9\overline{)18}$ $\quad$ $9\overline{)54}$ $\quad$ $3\overline{)21}$ $\quad$ $6\overline{)42}$ $\quad$ $3\overline{)9}$

$6\overline{)12}$ $\quad$ $3\overline{)3}$ $\quad$ $9\overline{)27}$ $\quad$ $3\overline{)15}$ $\quad$ $9\overline{)72}$

$6\overline{)24}$ $\quad$ $9\overline{)45}$ $\quad$ $3\overline{)24}$ $\quad$ $6\overline{)18}$ $\quad$ $3\overline{)0}$

$6\overline{)48}$ $\quad$ $3\overline{)12}$ $\quad$ $9\overline{)63}$ $\quad$ $9\overline{)9}$ $\quad$ $6\overline{)36}$

Score: _____

Name ●
(Draw a $3\frac{1}{4}$" line segment.)

Date ●——————————————●

(Measure this line segment using inches. _____")

1. How many days are there in 4 years?

    Number sentence _____ Answer _____

2. Fill in the missing numbers and write the rule.

S	6	9	13	21	27	54	100	S
T	1	4			22	49		

3. Find the answers.

    $7\overline{)41}$ $5\overline{)32}$ $\frac{23}{3} =$ $\frac{20}{6} =$

4. Draw a line segment that is perpendicular to $\overline{AB}$. Label the endpoints C and D. $A \bullet \!\!-\!\!\!-\!\!\!-\!\! \bullet B$

5. These are cakes. Divide each cake into four pieces.

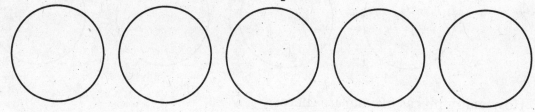

    How many pieces of cake are there? _____

    The children ate $3\frac{3}{4}$ cakes. Color the cake they ate.

    How much cake is left? _____

6. Find each answer.

    2,624 + 948   800 − 516 $\begin{array}{r} 25 \\ \times\ 6 \\ \hline \end{array}$ $\begin{array}{r} 389 \\ \times\ 5 \\ \hline \end{array}$

3-126Wa

Name _____ **LESSON 126B**

Date _____ *Math 3*

1. How many days are there in 5 years?

   Number sentence _____ Answer _____

2. Fill in the missing numbers and write the rule.

U	4	7	11	9	22	43	59	100	U
V	15	18			33	54			

3. Find the answers.

   $4\overline{)25}$ $\qquad$ $9\overline{)49}$ $\qquad$ $\dfrac{22}{7} =$ $\qquad$ $\dfrac{38}{5} =$

4. Draw a line segment that is parallel to $\overline{AB}$.
   Label the endpoints E and F.

5. These are cakes. Divide each cake into eight pieces.

   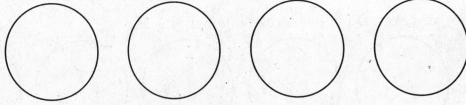

   How many pieces of cake are there? _____

   The children ate $2\frac{3}{8}$ cakes. Color the cake they ate.

   How much cake is left? _____

6. Find each answer.

   $5,637 + 845$ $\qquad$ $300 - 12$ $\qquad$ $\begin{array}{r} 32 \\ \times\ 4 \\ \hline \end{array}$ $\qquad$ $\begin{array}{r} 245 \\ \times\ 7 \\ \hline \end{array}$

Name _____

Today's Problem

Coin Cup

Q	D	N	P	Total Coins

Today's Date is _____

Today's Pattern _____

_____

Today's Problem

Coin Cup

Q	D	N	P	Total Coins

Today's Date is _____

Today's Pattern _____

_____

Today's Problem

Coin Cup

Q	D	N	P	Total Coins

Today's Date is _____

Today's Pattern _____

_____

Today's Problem

Coin Cup

Q	D	N	P	Total Coins

Today's Date is _____

Today's Pattern _____

_____

Today's Problem

Coin Cup

Q	D	N	P	Total Coins

Today's Date is _____

Today's Pattern _____

_____

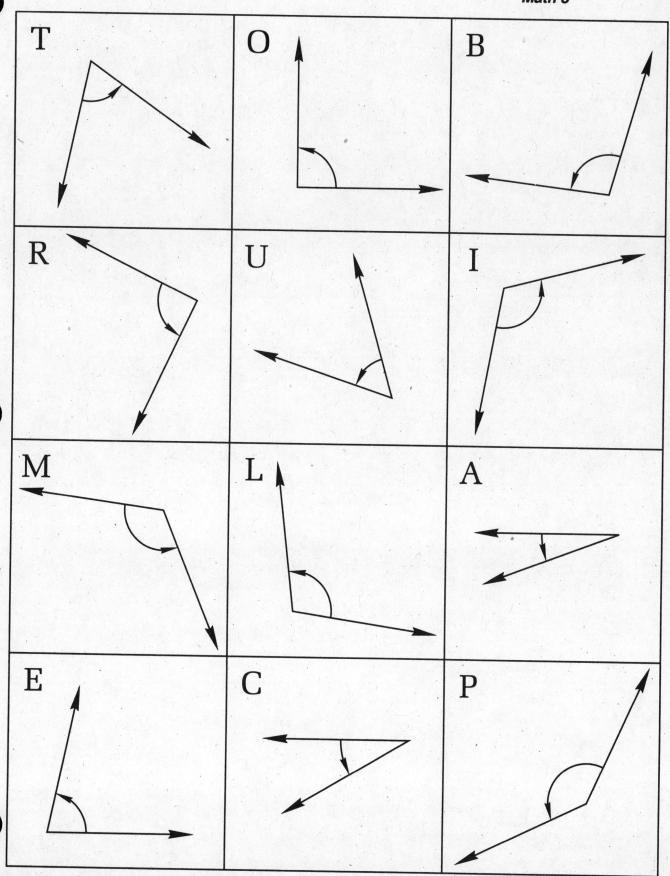

●

$$\frac{18}{6} =$$ $$\frac{27}{9} =$$ $$\frac{6}{3} =$$ $$\frac{63}{9} =$$ $$\frac{12}{3} =$$

$$\frac{24}{6} =$$ $$\frac{21}{3} =$$ $$\frac{30}{6} =$$ $$\frac{18}{9} =$$ $$\frac{54}{6} =$$

●$$\frac{24}{3} =$$ $$\frac{36}{9} =$$ $$\frac{0}{3} =$$ $$\frac{81}{9} =$$ $$\frac{42}{6} =$$

$$\frac{72}{9} =$$ $$\frac{48}{6} =$$ $$\frac{27}{3} =$$ $$\frac{12}{6} =$$ $$\frac{15}{3} =$$

●$$\frac{45}{9} =$$ $$\frac{18}{3} =$$ $$\frac{36}{6} =$$ $$\frac{54}{9} =$$ $$\frac{3}{3} =$$

Name ●
    (Draw a $3\frac{3}{4}$" line segment.)

Date ●————————————————————●

(Measure this line segment using inches. _____")

1. There are twenty-six weeks in half of a year. How many days are there in twenty-six weeks?

   Number sentence _____ Answer _____

2. Circle the shape with a perimeter of 14 cm. Color the shapes with area(s) of 12 square centimeters red.

3. Label each angle (acute, right, or obtuse).

   _____   _____   _____

4. Show eleven twenty-nine on the clocks.
   It's morning.
   What time will it
   be 1 hour from now? _____

5. Write a multiplication number sentence for this picture.

   _____

   Write a division example for this picture. ⟌‾‾‾‾

   ▱ = 1 cupcake

6. Find the answers.

   $3\overline{)23}$ $9\overline{)34}$ $2 \times 6,172$ $900 - 123$

Name _____   **LESSON 127B**
                                                    Math 3
Date _____

1. How many days are there in thirty-five weeks?

   Number sentence _____   Answer _____

2. Circle the shape with a perimeter of 10 cm. Color the shape with an area of 9 square centimeters red.

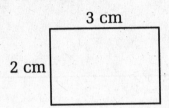

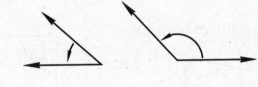

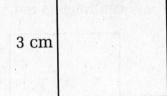

3. Label each angle (acute, right, or obtuse).

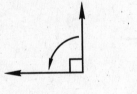

   _____   _____   _____

4. Show twelve fifty-three on the clocks.
   It's afternoon.
   What time was it 1 hour ago? _____

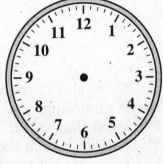

5. Write a multiplication number sentence for this picture.

   _____

   Write a division example for this picture.

   ⬭ = 1 cupcake

6. Find the answers.

   5)‾19‾   8)‾37‾   3 × 2,109   800 − 428

Name _____ Score: _____ **M-100**

6	2	7	4	1	9	3	8	0	9
×1	×5	×0	×4	×2	×5	×3	×5	×4	×9

1	7	3	8	0	4	9	2	4	9
×5	×4	×2	×9	×3	×1	×3	×6	×8	×0

5	6	0	9	4	2	6	3	9	6
×2	×3	×7	×2	×7	×3	×9	×5	×1	×4

7	2	6	1	9	3	7	0	8	4
×7	×9	×5	×8	×4	×6	×9	×6	×1	×2

4	1	5	3	7	2	6	5	1	8
×9	×1	×0	×8	×5	×4	×6	×3	×0	×8

4	7	2	5	6	0	3	4	8	3
×3	×8	×1	×4	×6	×0	×7	×4	×6	×1

2	3	9	6	1	4	8	0	3	7
×7	×0	×9	×7	×3	×5	×3	×1	×3	×2

3	8	0	5	7	1	5	2	6	7
×9	×4	×2	×5	×6	×6	×5	×2	×8	×1

8	1	9	4	8	7	0	5	6	4
×2	×7	×8	×6	×0	×3	×9	×6	×2	×0

0	9	3	8	2	5	6	1	8	5
×8	×6	×4	×7	×0	×7	×0	×4	×8	×9

3-128Fa

Name •

(Draw an 8 cm 2 mm line segment.)

Date •————————————————————————•

(Measure this line segment using centimeters. _____ cm _____ mm)

1. Jeremy is three years older than his brother and two years younger than his sister. His brother is 7. How old is Jeremy?

   Number sentence _____

   Answer _____

   How old is Jeremy's sister?

   Number sentence _____

   Answer _____

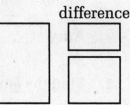

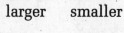

2. Find the answers.

   $\frac{3}{5} + \frac{1}{5} =$ ____ $\frac{2}{7} + \frac{3}{7} =$ ____ $\frac{6}{8} - \frac{1}{8} =$ ____

3. The minute hand is pointing to the twelve.
   The hour hand is perpendicular.

   What two times could it be? _____ _____
   Show one of the times on the clock.

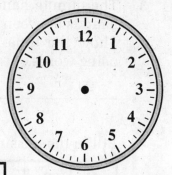

4. Fill in the missing numbers and write the rule.

M	2	8	14	6	12	20	100	M
N	1	4	7			10		

5. Label each angle (right, obtuse, or acute).

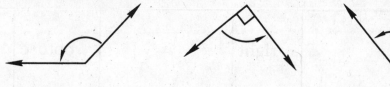

_____   _____   _____

6. Find the answers.

   248 + 365 + 729   800 − 208   7)‾44‾   4 × 2,071

Name _____

Date _____

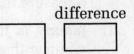

1. Lee is four years younger than his sister and one year older than his brother. His sister is 10. How old is Lee?

    Number sentence _____

    Answer _____

    How old is Lee's brother?

    Number sentence _____

    Answer _____

    difference

    larger   smaller

    _____ _____

    difference

    larger   smaller

    _____ _____

2. Find the answers.

    $\dfrac{1}{3} + \dfrac{1}{3} =$ ____ $\dfrac{4}{9} + \dfrac{3}{9} =$ ____ $\dfrac{5}{7} - \dfrac{2}{7} =$ ____

3. The minute hand is on the nine and the hour hand is between the 5 and 6.
    Show the time on the clock. Write the time using words.

    _____

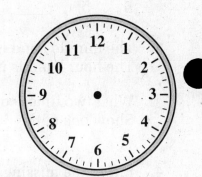

4. Fill in the missing numbers and write the rule.

P	2	6	3	7	12	8	20	100	P
Q	6	18	9				60		

5. Draw an example of each type of angle.

    acute   right   obtuse

6. Find the answers.

    $492 + 314 + 588$ $900 - 104$ $4\overline{)31}$ $3 \times 6{,}104$

3-128Wb

$16 \div 4 =$

$48 \div 8 =$

$24 \div 8 =$

$40 \div 8 =$

$12 \div 4 =$

$32 \div 8 =$

$12 \div 4 =$

$20 \div 4 =$

$4 \div 4 =$

$0 \div 4 =$

$0 \div 4 =$

$72 \div 8 =$

$28 \div 4 =$

$56 \div 8 =$

$72 \div 8 =$

$8 \div 4 =$

$16 \div 8 =$

$8 \div 8 =$

$0 \div 8 =$

$28 \div 4 =$

$40 \div 8 =$

$36 \div 4 =$

$64 \div 8 =$

$24 \div 4 =$

$16 \div 4 =$

Score: _____

3-129Fa

Name _____ •

(Draw a 109 mm line segment.)

Date •————————————————•

(Measure this line segment using millimeters. _____ mm)

1. Keith has 324 pennies, Michael has 269 pennies, and Willie has 185 pennies. How many pennies do the three boys have altogether?

   Number sentence _____ Answer _____

   How many more pennies does Keith have than Willie?

   Number sentence _____ Answer _____

2. Curtis gave the clerk $1.00 for a 73¢ marker.

   How much change did he receive? _____

3. Carol's family ate $1\frac{1}{4}$ cakes. Color the cakes to show how much cake they ate.

   How much cake is left? _____

   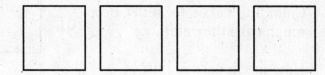

4. Find each answer.

   $4 \times 3,802$ 143 $3\overline{)88}$ $5\overline{)92}$
                         $\times\ 7$

5. Find the answers.

   $\frac{7}{12} - \frac{5}{12} =$ _____ $462.93 + $75.35 $700 - $251

Name _____

Date _____

1. Flavia has 193 dimes, Carmela has 227 dimes, and Karen has 176 dimes. How many dimes do the girls have altogether?

   Number sentence _____ Answer _____

   How many more dimes than Karen does Carmela have?

   Number sentence _____ Answer _____

2. Terri gave the clerk $1.00 for a 38¢ pencil.

   How much change did she receive? _____

3. Sandy's family ate $2\frac{1}{3}$ cakes. Color the cakes to show how much cake they ate.

   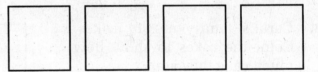

   How much cake is left? _____

4. Find each answer.

   $8 \times 2,450$ $\begin{array}{r} 293 \\ \times\ 9 \\ \hline \end{array}$ $6\overline{)83}$ $4\overline{)87}$

5. Find the answers.

   $\frac{5}{9} - \frac{3}{9} =$ _____ $\$91.82 + \$253.47$ $\$800 - \$559$

Name ●————————————————————————————————————●

(Measure this line segment using inches. _____")

Date ●————————————————————————————————————●

(Measure this line segment using centimeters. _____ cm)

1. Carol has 354 nickels, Doug has 291 nickels, and Anna has 179 nickels. How many nickels do the children have altogether?

   Number sentence _____ Answer _____

2. Use the information in Problem 1 to answer this question. How many more nickels than Anna does Doug have?

   Number sentence _____ Answer _____

3. How many days are there in twenty-five weeks?

   Number sentence _____ Answer _____

4. Write the number sentences to match the number lines.

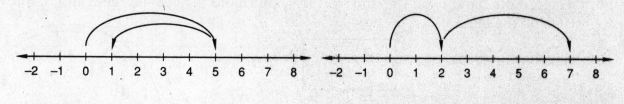

   _____   _____

5. Fill in the missing numbers and write the rule.

G	5	3	8	11	15	20	100	G
H	2		5		12			

6. Find each answer.

   $3,714.26 + 629.86 $800 − $137   7 × 3,209

7. Find the perimeter and area of this rectangle.

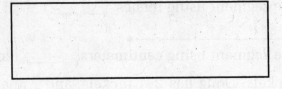

Perimeter = _____ cm

Area = _____ square centimeters

8. Find the answers.

$\frac{16}{2} =$ 5⟌40   42 ÷ 7 = $\frac{8}{2} =$

7⟌56   45 ÷ 5 = $\frac{35}{7} =$ 2⟌18

9. The minute hand is on the nine and the hour hand is between the 2 and 3. Show the time on the clocks.

Write the time using words. _____

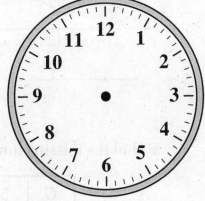

10. Finish the number patterns and write the rules.

_____ , _____ , _____ , 824, 724, 624, _____ , _____ , _____   Rule: _____

_____ , _____ , _____ , _____ , _____ , _____ , 38, 43, 48   Rule: _____

How far is it from . . .	Inches on Map	Miles
Sacramento, **California** to Carson City, **Nevada**		
Des Moines, **Iowa** to Madison, **Wisconsin**		
Cheyenne, **Wyoming** to Denver, **Colorado**		
Boise, **Idaho** to Helena, **Montana**		
Nashville, **Tennessee** to Atlanta, **Georgia**		
Jackson, **Mississippi** to Montgomery, **Alabama**		
Springfield, **Illinois** to Lansing, **Michigan**		
Santa Fe, **New Mexico** to Austin, **Texas**		
Richmond, **Virginia** to Raleigh, **North Carolina**		

What is your capital city? _____

Can you find other capital cities that are approximately the following distances away?

100 miles _____

200 miles _____

300 miles _____

$4\overline{)24}$ $8\overline{)8}$ $4\overline{)16}$ $8\overline{)40}$ $8\overline{)72}$

$4\overline{)4}$ $8\overline{)32}$ $4\overline{)0}$ $4\overline{)20}$ $8\overline{)16}$

$8\overline{)24}$ $8\overline{)48}$ $4\overline{)28}$ $4\overline{)8}$ $8\overline{)0}$

$4\overline{)12}$ $8\overline{)56}$ $4\overline{)32}$ $8\overline{)40}$ $4\overline{)12}$

$8\overline{)24}$ $8\overline{)16}$ $8\overline{)72}$ $4\overline{)28}$ $4\overline{)4}$

Score: _____

Name

Today's Date is _____

Today's Pattern
_____
_____

Coin Cup

Q	D	N	P	Total Coins

Today's Problem

Today's Date is _____

Today's Pattern
_____
_____

Coin Cup

Q	D	N	P	Total Coins

Today's Problem

Today's Date is _____

Today's Pattern
_____
_____

Coin Cup

Q	D	N	P	Total Coins

Today's Problem

Today's Date is _____

Today's Pattern
_____
_____

Coin Cup

Q	D	N	P	Total Coins

Today's Problem

Today's Date is _____

Today's Pattern
_____
_____

Coin Cup

Q	D	N	P	Total Coins

Today's Problem

● $\dfrac{20}{4} =$ $\dfrac{64}{8} =$ $\dfrac{4}{4} =$ $\dfrac{0}{8} =$ $\dfrac{24}{4} =$

$\dfrac{40}{8} =$ $\dfrac{8}{4} =$ $\dfrac{32}{8} =$ $\dfrac{36}{4} =$ $\dfrac{8}{8} =$

● $\dfrac{0}{4} =$ $\dfrac{28}{4} =$ $\dfrac{16}{8} =$ $\dfrac{56}{8} =$ $\dfrac{32}{4} =$

$\dfrac{24}{8} =$ $\dfrac{16}{4} =$ $\dfrac{20}{4} =$ $\dfrac{48}{8} =$ $\dfrac{0}{8} =$

● $\dfrac{36}{4} =$ $\dfrac{64}{8} =$ $\dfrac{0}{4} =$ $\dfrac{24}{4} =$ $\dfrac{8}{8} =$

Name ●
    (Draw a 9 cm 5 mm line segment.)

Date ●

    (Draw a 95 mm line segment.)

1. David's team scored 73 points. They won by 17 points. How many points did the other team score?

    Number sentence _____

    Answer _____

    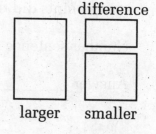

    difference

    larger   smaller

    _____

2. Show ten minutes of three on the clocks.

3. Write the factors of each number. Circle all the prime numbers. (Prime numbers have exactly 2 factors.)

    14   5   18

    _____   _____   _____

4. Circle the triangle that has an obtuse angle.
    Put an ✗ in the triangle that has a right angle.
    Put a ✓ in the triangle that only has acute angles.

5. I have 5 quarters, 8 dimes, 4 nickels, and 2 pennies. Draw the coins.

    How much money is this? _____

6. Find the answers.

    $\frac{3}{5} + \frac{1}{5} =$ $\frac{7}{8} - \frac{6}{8} =$ $6\overline{)93}$ $\frac{21}{4} =$

Name _____   **LESSON 131B**

Date _____   **Math 3**

1. Christa's team scored 56 points. They lost by 15 points. How   difference
    many points did the other team score?

    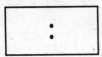

    Number sentence _____

    Answer _____   larger   smaller

                                                        _____

2. Show twenty minutes
    of five on the clocks.

    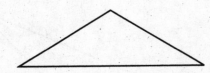 

3. Write the factors of each number. Circle all the prime numbers. (Prime numbers have
    exactly 2 factors.)

            7   8   15

    _____   _____   _____

4. Circle the triangle that has an obtuse angle.
    Put an ✗ in the triangle that has a right angle.
    Put a ✓ in the triangle that only has acute angles.

5. I have 6 quarters, 4 dimes, 5 nickels, and 3 pennies. Draw the coins.

    How much money is this? _____

6. Find the answers.

    $\frac{5}{8} + \frac{2}{8} =$ $\frac{3}{4} - \frac{2}{4} =$ $8\overline{)73}$ $\frac{20}{3} =$

Name _____   Score: _____   **S-100**

7 − 1	10 − 4	9 − 0	16 − 9	5 − 4	12 − 6	9 − 7	11 − 3	8 − 2	6 − 6
9 − 4	6 − 3	11 − 6	10 − 2	6 − 1	12 − 8	2 − 0	9 − 3	7 − 2	6 − 5
5 − 5	11 − 4	4 − 2	15 − 9	8 − 0	10 − 6	14 − 5	9 − 9	7 − 6	12 − 7
9 − 5	17 − 9	8 − 4	13 − 8	9 − 2	11 − 5	15 − 6	5 − 1	8 − 5	16 − 8
8 − 6	11 − 7	1 − 0	7 − 3	9 − 6	4 − 3	17 − 8	10 − 5	12 − 4	13 − 7
8 − 3	16 − 7	10 − 3	4 − 1	6 − 2	13 − 5	7 − 0	14 − 9	11 − 2	10 − 8
13 − 9	10 − 7	18 − 9	14 − 6	1 − 1	12 − 3	7 − 5	4 − 1	11 − 8	7 − 7
2 − 2	12 − 5	3 − 1	15 − 7	10 − 1	6 − 0	13 − 4	5 − 2	9 − 8	3 − 0
11 − 9	7 − 6	13 − 6	3 − 3	14 − 8	9 − 1	6 − 4	12 − 9	7 − 4	8 − 7
4 − 4	15 − 8	3 − 2	5 − 0	5 − 3	8 − 8	14 − 7	10 − 9	0 − 0	8 − 1

3-132Fa

9 ÷ 3 =

6 ÷ 6 =

18 ÷ 9 =

36 ÷ 6 =

15 ÷ 3 =

72 ÷ 9 =

24 ÷ 3 =

30 ÷ 6 =

12 ÷ 3 =

45 ÷ 9 =

27 ÷ 9 =

0 ÷ 3 =

18 ÷ 6 =

9 ÷ 9 =

54 ÷ 6 =

21 ÷ 3 =

48 ÷ 6 =

63 ÷ 9 =

0 ÷ 6 =

3 ÷ 3 =

54 ÷ 9 =

6 ÷ 3 =

24 ÷ 6 =

18 ÷ 3 =

81 ÷ 9 =

Score: _____

3-132Fb

Name **●**

(Draw a line segment $3\frac{1}{2}$" long.)

Date **●**

(Draw a line segment 2" longer than the name line.)

●

1. If each child in our class has 6 dimes, how many dimes will we have?

    Number sentence _____ Answer _____

    How much money will that be? _____

2. Use your ruler to find the perimeter of the rectangle below in inches.

    Perimeter = _____

3. Draw a 2 by 6 array of **✗**'s.

    How many **✗**'s did you draw? _____

●

4. What is a prime number greater than 8 but less than 12? _____

5. Write each example without exponents. Find the answers.

    $3^2 =$ _____ $5^2 =$ _____ $7^2 =$ _____

    _____   _____   _____

6.   Draw parallel lines.   Draw perpendicular lines.

7. Find the answers.

    $5\overline{)79}$ $7\overline{)64}$

    $3 \times 5 \times 2 =$ _____

    $2 \times 6 \times 3 =$ _____

    ```
      5 8 2.1 7
      4 7 3.4 3
    + 5 8.2 6
    ```

    ```
      5,628
    ×     4
    ```

●

Name _____

Date _____

1. Each child has 4 dimes. If there are 35 children, how many dimes will they have?

    Number sentence _____ Answer _____

    How much money is that? _____

2. Find the perimeter of this rectangle.   2 cm

    Perimeter = _____

3 cm

3. Draw a 3 by 5 array of ✗'s.

    How many ✗'s did you draw? _____

4. What is a prime number greater than 14 but less than 18? _____

5. Write each example without exponents. Find the answers.

    $4^2 =$ _____ $6^2 =$ _____ $9^2 =$ _____

    _____   _____   _____

6. Find examples of parallel and perpendicular lines at home. What did you find?

    parallel _____   perpendicular _____

    _____   _____

    _____   _____

7. Find the answers.

                              $8 \times 5 \times 3 =$ ____   2 9 3.1 2
                                                                    4 7.3 4
    $4\overline{)72}$ $9\overline{)85}$ $+\ 3 8 8.2 9$ 1,765
                                                                                            $\times\ 5$
                              $4 \times 2 \times 7 =$ ____   _____   _____

$3\overline{)6}$ $\qquad$ $9\overline{)81}$ $\qquad$ $6\overline{)30}$ $\qquad$ $6\overline{)0}$ $\qquad$ $3\overline{)27}$

$9\overline{)18}$ $\qquad$ $9\overline{)54}$ $\qquad$ $3\overline{)21}$ $\qquad$ $6\overline{)42}$ $\qquad$ $3\overline{)9}$

$6\overline{)12}$ $\qquad$ $3\overline{)3}$ $\qquad$ $9\overline{)27}$ $\qquad$ $3\overline{)15}$ $\qquad$ $9\overline{)72}$

$6\overline{)24}$ $\qquad$ $9\overline{)45}$ $\qquad$ $3\overline{)24}$ $\qquad$ $6\overline{)18}$ $\qquad$ $3\overline{)0}$

$6\overline{)48}$ $\qquad$ $3\overline{)12}$ $\qquad$ $9\overline{)63}$ $\qquad$ $9\overline{)9}$ $\qquad$ $6\overline{)36}$

Score: _____

Name .

(Draw a $3\frac{1}{2}$" line segment.)

Date .

(Draw a $3\frac{2}{4}$" line segment.)

1. Ms. Mallone bought four markers and four notebooks. The cost of each marker is 68¢. The cost of each notebook is 89¢. How much money did she spend?

   Number sentence _____

   Answer _____

Markers	Notebooks

2. Draw lines of symmetry in these shapes.

   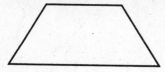 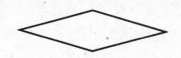

   Trace a pair of parallel line segments in each shape using a red crayon.

3. Write the factors of each number. Circle all the prime numbers. (Prime numbers have exactly 2 factors.)

   10   13

   _____   _____

4. What types of angles (right, obtuse, or acute) do the hands on these clocks make?

   _____   _____   _____

5. Write the digital time for each clock.

   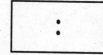 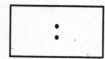 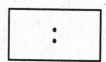

6. Find the answers.

   $\frac{4}{5} - \frac{3}{5} =$ 9×304 $\begin{array}{r} 409 \\ - 57 \\ \hline \end{array}$ $3\overline{)58}$ $7\overline{)52}$

3-133Wa

Name _____

Date _____

1. Scott bought three bags of chips and eight hot dogs. The bags of chips cost 59¢ each and the hot dogs cost 98¢ each. How much money did he spend altogether?

Chips	Hot dogs

   Number sentence _____

   Answer _____

2. Draw lines of symmetry in these shapes.

 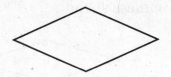

   Trace a pair of parallel lines using a red crayon.

3. Write the factors of each number. Circle all the prime numbers. (Prime numbers have exactly 2 factors.)

   6   17

   _____   _____

4. What types of angles (right, obtuse, or acute) do the hands on these clocks make?

   _____   _____   _____

5. Write the digital time for each clock.

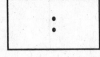 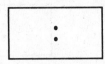

6. Find the answers.

$$\frac{3}{4} - \frac{2}{4} =$$ 8×409 $\begin{array}{r} 7\,0\,2 \\ -\ 5\,1 \\ \hline \end{array}$ $6\overline{)23}$ $5\overline{)72}$

Name _____   Score: _____   **D 19.2**

$\dfrac{18}{6} =$ $\dfrac{27}{9} =$ $\dfrac{6}{3} =$ $\dfrac{63}{9} =$ $\dfrac{12}{3} =$

$\dfrac{24}{6} =$ $\dfrac{21}{3} =$ $\dfrac{30}{6} =$ $\dfrac{18}{9} =$ $\dfrac{54}{6} =$

$\dfrac{24}{3} =$ $\dfrac{36}{9} =$ $\dfrac{0}{3} =$ $\dfrac{81}{9} =$ $\dfrac{42}{6} =$

$\dfrac{72}{9} =$ $\dfrac{48}{6} =$ $\dfrac{27}{3} =$ $\dfrac{12}{6} =$ $\dfrac{15}{3} =$

$\dfrac{45}{9} =$ $\dfrac{18}{3} =$ $\dfrac{36}{6} =$ $\dfrac{54}{9} =$ $\dfrac{3}{3} =$

Name •————————————————————• (Measure this line segment. _____ cm)

•
(Draw a line segment 2 cm shorter than the name line. _____ cm)

1. Forty-two children are going to the play. Each car will hold 5 children. How many cars are needed for the trip?

   Number sentence _____ Answer _____

2. Write the letter **A** inside an acute angle.

   Write the letter **R** inside a right angle.

   Write the letter **O** inside an obtuse angle.

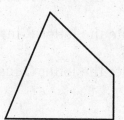

3. Show seventeen minutes of eight on the clocks.

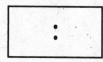

4. There are 8 people waiting for a conference with Mrs. Holt. I am fourth. Each person's conference will take 5 minutes.

   How long will I have to wait? _____

   How long will the last person have to wait? _____

5. Find the answers.

   $2\overline{)694}$ $3\overline{)714}$ $6\overline{)93}$ $8^2 =$ ____ $5^2 =$ ____

6. Fill in the missing numbers. Write the rules.

   _____ , _____ , _____ , 236, 247, 258, _____ , _____ , _____   Rule: _____

   $\frac{1}{4}$, $\frac{2}{4}$, $\frac{3}{4}$, 1, $1\frac{1}{4}$, _____ , _____ , _____ , _____ , _____   Rule: _____

Name _____ **LESSON 134B**
                                                    Math 3
Date _____

1. There are 26 children in the class. Each table can seat 4 children. How many tables will be needed to seat the children in the class?

   Number sentence _____ Answer _____

2. Write the letter **A** inside an acute angle.

   Write the letter **R** inside a right angle.

   Write the letter **O** inside an obtuse angle.

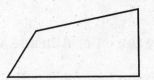

3. Show eleven minutes of one on the clocks.

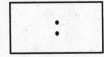

4. There are 10 people waiting for a conference with Mrs. Saunders. I am sixth. Each person's conference will take 5 minutes.

   How long will I have to wait? _____

   How long will the last person have to wait? _____

5. Find the answers.

   $4\overline{)553}$ $5\overline{)720}$ $8\overline{)93}$ $9^2 =$ _____ $7^2 =$ _____

6. Fill in the missing numbers. Write the rules.

   _____ , _____ , _____ , 348, 337, 326, _____ , _____ , _____   Rule: _____

   $\frac{1}{3}$, $\frac{2}{3}$, 1 , $1\frac{1}{3}$, $1\frac{2}{3}$, 2, _____ , _____ , _____ , _____ , _____   Rule: _____

Name _____

Section 1

Today's Problem _____

Coin Cup

Q	D	N	P	Total Coins

Today's Date is _____

Today's Pattern _____

_____

Section 2

Today's Problem _____

Coin Cup

Q	D	N	P	Total Coins

Today's Date is _____

Today's Pattern _____

_____

Section 3

Today's Problem _____

Coin Cup

Q	D	N	P	Total Coins

Today's Date is _____

Today's Pattern _____

_____

Section 4

Today's Problem _____

Coin Cup

Q	D	N	P	Total Coins

Today's Date is _____

Today's Pattern _____

_____

Section 5

Today's Problem _____

Coin Cup

Q	D	N	P	Total Coins

Today's Date is _____

Today's Pattern _____

_____

3-*R1Ma

Name _____

Date _____

1. Two hundred fifteen children ordered pizza, one hundred seven children ordered hamburgers, and ninety-eight children ordered hot dogs. How many children ordered hot dogs and hamburgers?

    Number sentence _____ Answer _____

2. Each child has a box of 48 crayons. If there are 7 children, how many crayons are there altogether?

    Number sentence _____ Answer _____

3. Find the answers.

    $\frac{3}{5} + \frac{1}{5} =$ _____ $\frac{2}{3} - \frac{1}{3} =$ _____ $\frac{7}{10} + \frac{2}{10} =$ _____

4. Write a letter of the alphabet that has parallel line segments. Trace the parallel line segments with a crayon.

    Write a letter of the alphabet that has perpendicular line segments. Trace the perpendicular line segments with a crayon.

5. Find the answers.

    $4\overline{)29}$ $8\overline{)50}$ $\frac{16}{3}$

6. Measure each line segment.

    _____ cm _____ mm

    ●——●

    _____ "

    ●——●

    Draw these line segments.

    52 mm ●

    $2\frac{1}{4}"$ ●

7. Label each angle (right, obtuse, or acute).

_____   _____   _____

8. List all the factors of each number. Circle the prime numbers.

       10   5   1   18

_____   _____   _____   _____

9. I have 3 quarters, 7 dimes, 1 nickel, and 6 pennies. Draw the coins.

How much money is this? _____

10. Find the answers.

$$\begin{array}{r} 1\,2\,8.4\,2 \\ 3\,7.1\,9 \\ +\ 3\,6\,5.3\,1 \\ \hline \end{array}$$

204 − 58 = _____

6 × 498 = _____

6 ÷ 3 =	20 ÷ 5 =	9 ÷ 9 =	12 ÷ 4 =	10 ÷ 2 =
40 ÷ 8 =	1 ÷ 1 =	36 ÷ 6 =	63 ÷ 7 =	16 ÷ 4 =
35 ÷ 5 =	6 ÷ 1 =	18 ÷ 3 =	21 ÷ 7 =	81 ÷ 9 =
6 ÷ 2 =	16 ÷ 8 =	20 ÷ 4 =	7 ÷ 1 =	54 ÷ 6 =
6 ÷ 6 =	40 ÷ 5 =	9 ÷ 1 =	0 ÷ 8 =	27 ÷ 3 =
64 ÷ 8 =	14 ÷ 7 =	8 ÷ 2 =	0 ÷ 4 =	27 ÷ 9 =
24 ÷ 8 =	15 ÷ 3 =	16 ÷ 2 =	45 ÷ 9 =	18 ÷ 6 =
2 ÷ 1 =	25 ÷ 5 =	12 ÷ 3 =	16 ÷ 4 =	56 ÷ 7 =
25 ÷ 5 =	16 ÷ 2 =	7 ÷ 7 =	32 ÷ 4 =	72 ÷ 8 =
4 ÷ 2 =	30 ÷ 6 =	12 ÷ 3 =	18 ÷ 9 =	6 ÷ 6 =
5 ÷ 1 =	8 ÷ 8 =	36 ÷ 4 =	0 ÷ 2 =	54 ÷ 9 =
35 ÷ 7 =	9 ÷ 3 =	5 ÷ 5 =	12 ÷ 6 =	24 ÷ 3 =
24 ÷ 6 =	7 ÷ 1 =	30 ÷ 5 =	21 ÷ 3 =	6 ÷ 6 =
14 ÷ 2 =	72 ÷ 9 =	8 ÷ 4 =	0 ÷ 7 =	48 ÷ 8 =
63 ÷ 9 =	3 ÷ 3 =	28 ÷ 7 =	3 ÷ 1 =	42 ÷ 6 =
4 ÷ 4 =	32 ÷ 8 =	2 ÷ 2 =	36 ÷ 9 =	0 ÷ 5 =
12 ÷ 2 =	42 ÷ 7 =	10 ÷ 5 =	24 ÷ 4 =	8 ÷ 1 =
49 ÷ 7 =	9 ÷ 3 =	0 ÷ 9 =	12 ÷ 6 =	56 ÷ 8 =
28 ÷ 4 =	24 ÷ 8 =	0 ÷ 3 =	48 ÷ 6 =	10 ÷ 2 =
18 ÷ 9 =	4 ÷ 1 =	25 ÷ 5 =	48 ÷ 8 =	21 ÷ 7 =

3-135Fa

Name ●——————————————●
(Measure this line segment using inches. _____ ")

● Date ●——————————————●
(Measure this line segment using centimeters. _____ cm)

1. The children in Ms. Mursko's room had a race. Michael finished in 54 seconds, Peter finished in 48 seconds, and Erica finished in 39 seconds. How much longer did it take Michael than Erica?

   Number sentence _____ Answer _____

2. Simplify each expression. (Remember: Simplify the multiplication and division first.)

   $16 \div 4 - 2 + 7 \times 3 =$ $20 - 18 \div 2 + 6 \times 3 =$

3. Draw lines of symmetry in the rectangle.

● 4. List the months with 31 days.

   _____

   _____

   What fractional part of the months of the year have 31 days? _____

5. Find the answers.

   $\begin{array}{r} 5\,4\,3 \\ \times\ 7 \\ \hline \end{array}$ $\begin{array}{r} 8\,2\,9\,3 \\ \times\ 6 \\ \hline \end{array}$ $4\overline{)96}$ $5\overline{)806}$ $3\overline{)236}$

6. Use the graph to answer the questions.

   About how many dogs are there? _____

   About how many cats are there? _____

   ● About how many birds are there? _____

   About how many pets are there altogether? _____

NUMBER OF PETS

Dogs
Cats
Birds

0 10 20 30 40 50 60

3-135Wa

Name _____   **LESSON 135B**
                                          Math 3

Date _____

1. Danielle's ribbon is 85 cm long, Lee's ribbon is 57 cm long, and Shawnee's ribbon is 72 cm long. How much longer is Shawnee's ribbon than Lee's?

    Number sentence _____ Answer _____

2. Simplify each expression. (Remember: Simplify the multiplication and division first.)

    $8 + 12 \div 4 - 3 \times 2 =$ $4 \times 6 - 12 \div 3 + 7 =$

3. Draw lines of symmetry in the square.

4. List the months with exactly 30 days.

    _____

    _____

    What fractional part of the months of the year have exactly 30 days? _____

5. Find the answers.

    $\begin{array}{r} 326 \\ \times\ 8 \\ \hline \end{array}$ $\begin{array}{r} 2541 \\ \times\ 9 \\ \hline \end{array}$ $6\overline{)96}$ $4\overline{)903}$ $8\overline{)742}$

6. Use the graph to answer the questions.

    About how many dogs are there? _____

    About how many cats are there? _____

    About how many birds are there? _____

    About how many pets are there altogether? _____

    NUMBER OF PETS

    Dogs
    Cats
    Birds

    0 10 20 30 40 50 60

Name _____

1.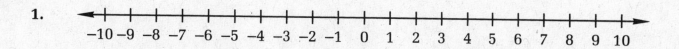

2.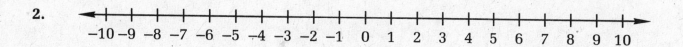

3.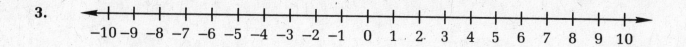

4.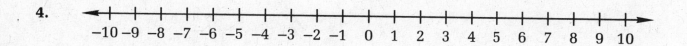

5.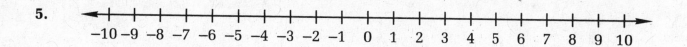

6.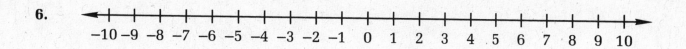

7.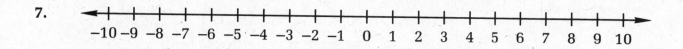

8.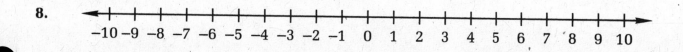

● $5\overline{)15}$ $2\overline{)8}$ $7\overline{)49}$ $1\overline{)3}$ $6\overline{)6}$ $9\overline{)27}$ $5\overline{)30}$ $4\overline{)12}$ $8\overline{)32}$ $3\overline{)21}$

$2\overline{)2}$ $5\overline{)40}$ $9\overline{)72}$ $3\overline{)3}$ $7\overline{)28}$ $4\overline{)4}$ $8\overline{)16}$ $3\overline{)6}$ $6\overline{)42}$ $1\overline{)1}$

$4\overline{)24}$ $7\overline{)0}$ $3\overline{)15}$ $8\overline{)48}$ $2\overline{)4}$ $6\overline{)24}$ $1\overline{)7}$ $9\overline{)18}$ $5\overline{)25}$ $2\overline{)0}$

$6\overline{)18}$ $9\overline{)45}$ $2\overline{)12}$ $5\overline{)5}$ $3\overline{)18}$ $7\overline{)56}$ $1\overline{)0}$ $4\overline{)36}$ $6\overline{)12}$ $8\overline{)40}$

$7\overline{)14}$ $1\overline{)2}$ $5\overline{)45}$ $2\overline{)10}$ $8\overline{)24}$ $4\overline{)0}$ $6\overline{)30}$ $3\overline{)12}$ $1\overline{)9}$ $9\overline{)36}$

● $9\overline{)9}$ $4\overline{)20}$ $6\overline{)48}$ $3\overline{)9}$ $5\overline{)0}$ $2\overline{)6}$ $8\overline{)64}$ $4\overline{)8}$ $1\overline{)6}$ $7\overline{)63}$

$3\overline{)24}$ $8\overline{)56}$ $2\overline{)18}$ $4\overline{)16}$ $9\overline{)54}$ $5\overline{)20}$ $1\overline{)5}$ $7\overline{)21}$ $8\overline{)72}$ $6\overline{)0}$

$5\overline{)10}$ $1\overline{)3}$ $9\overline{)63}$ $8\overline{)8}$ $3\overline{)27}$ $7\overline{)42}$ $2\overline{)16}$ $9\overline{)0}$ $6\overline{)18}$ $4\overline{)28}$

$1\overline{)4}$ $9\overline{)27}$ $7\overline{)35}$ $2\overline{)14}$ $6\overline{)36}$ $3\overline{)9}$ $8\overline{)0}$ $4\overline{)32}$ $5\overline{)30}$ $7\overline{)7}$

● $8\overline{)40}$ $6\overline{)36}$ $3\overline{)0}$ $9\overline{)72}$ $1\overline{)8}$ $5\overline{)15}$ $7\overline{)21}$ $2\overline{)16}$ $3\overline{)15}$ $4\overline{)24}$

Name _____   Score _____   **M-100**

6 × 1	2 × 5	7 × 0	4 × 4	1 × 2	9 × 5	3 × 3	8 × 5	0 × 4	9 × 9
1 × 5	7 × 4	3 × 2	8 × 9	0 × 3	4 × 1	9 × 3	2 × 6	4 × 8	9 × 0
5 × 2	6 × 3	0 × 7	9 × 2	4 × 7	2 × 3	6 × 9	3 × 5	9 × 1	6 × 4
7 × 7	2 × 9	6 × 5	1 × 8	9 × 4	3 × 6	7 × 9	0 × 6	8 × 1	4 × 2
4 × 9	1 × 1	5 × 0	3 × 8	7 × 5	2 × 4	6 × 6	5 × 3	1 × 0	8 × 8
4 × 3	7 × 8	2 × 1	5 × 4	6 × 6	0 × 0	3 × 7	4 × 4	8 × 6	3 × 1
2 × 7	3 × 0	9 × 9	6 × 7	1 × 3	4 × 5	8 × 3	0 × 1	3 × 3	7 × 2
3 × 9	8 × 4	0 × 2	5 × 5	7 × 6	1 × 6	5 × 5	2 × 2	6 × 8	7 × 1
8 × 2	1 × 7	9 × 8	4 × 6	8 × 0	7 × 3	0 × 9	5 × 6	6 × 2	4 × 0
0 × 8	9 × 6	3 × 4	8 × 7	2 × 0	5 × 7	6 × 0	1 × 4	8 × 8	5 × 9

Name _____

(Measure this line segment using inches. _____")

Date _____

(Measure this line segment using millimeters. _____ mm)

1. Ken collects stamps. He can put 4 stamps in each row in his book. There are 6 rows on each page. How many stamps can Ken put on a page? Draw a picture of the stamps on a page.

    Number sentence _____

    Answer _____

    How many stamps can he put on 10 pages?

    Number sentence _____ Answer _____

2. Draw a bar graph to show the number of children in each grade.

    Grade 1: 56 children

    Grade 2: 48 children

    Grade 3: 69 children

    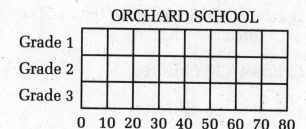

    How many fewer children will be in grade 3 next year? _____

3. Round each number to the nearest 10 and add or subtract the rounded numbers.

    47 + 35   78 – 39

    ____ + ____ = ____   ____ – ____ = ____

4. Find these answers using the number line.

    –3 + 4 = _____   –3 + –4 = _____

    -7 -6 -5 -4 -3 -2 -1 0 1 2 3 4 5 6 7   -7 -6 -5 -4 -3 -2 -1 0 1 2 3 4 5 6 7

5. Find the answers.

    8)‾983   4)‾357   400 – 31 = _____ $\frac{2}{7} + \frac{3}{7}$ = _____

Name _____   **LESSON 136B**
Date _____   Math 3

1. Elizabeth put her pictures in an album. She can put 3 pictures in each row. There are 3 rows on each page. How many pictures can Elizabeth put on a page? Draw a picture of the pictures on a page.

   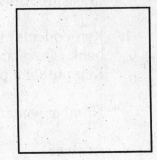

   Number sentence _____

   Answer _____

   How many pictures can she put on 10 pages?

   Number sentence _____ Answer _____

2. Draw a bar graph to show the number of children in each grade.

   Grade 4: 38 children

   Grade 5: 65 children

   Grade 6: 52 children

   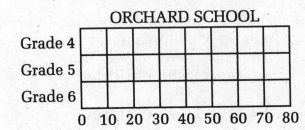

   How many more children will be in grade 6 next year? _____

3. Round each number to the nearest 10 and add or subtract the rounded numbers.

   45 + 23   42 – 19

   _____ + _____ = _____   _____ – _____ = _____

4. Find these answers using the number line.

   5 + –2 = _____   –5 + –2 = _____

   ![number line from -7 to 7]   ![number line from -7 to 7]
   –7 –6 –5 –4 –3 –2 –1 0 1 2 3 4 5 6 7   –7 –6 –5 –4 –3 –2 –1 0 1 2 3 4 5 6 7

5. Find the answers.

   $6\overline{)852}$ $3\overline{)196}$ $200 - 19 =$ _____ $\dfrac{6}{10} - \dfrac{3}{10} =$ _____

$\dfrac{49}{7} =$ $\quad$ $\dfrac{0}{4} =$ $\quad$ $\dfrac{24}{3} =$ $\quad$ $\dfrac{18}{6} =$ $\quad$ $\dfrac{0}{3} =$ $\quad$ $\dfrac{48}{8} =$ $\quad$ $\dfrac{24}{4} =$ $\quad$ $\dfrac{54}{9} =$ $\quad$ $\dfrac{42}{6} =$ $\quad$ $\dfrac{8}{2} =$

$\dfrac{0}{8} =$ $\quad$ $\dfrac{63}{7} =$ $\quad$ $\dfrac{40}{8} =$ $\quad$ $\dfrac{3}{1} =$ $\quad$ $\dfrac{63}{9} =$ $\quad$ $\dfrac{15}{5} =$ $\quad$ $\dfrac{6}{1} =$ $\quad$ $\dfrac{5}{5} =$ $\quad$ $\dfrac{10}{5} =$ $\quad$ $\dfrac{40}{8} =$

$\dfrac{9}{1} =$ $\quad$ $\dfrac{25}{5} =$ $\quad$ $\dfrac{18}{2} =$ $\quad$ $\dfrac{24}{8} =$ $\quad$ $\dfrac{25}{5} =$ $\quad$ $\dfrac{9}{3} =$ $\quad$ $\dfrac{9}{9} =$ $\quad$ $\dfrac{27}{3} =$ $\quad$ $\dfrac{56}{8} =$ $\quad$ $\dfrac{7}{1} =$

$\dfrac{3}{3} =$ $\quad$ $\dfrac{16}{8} =$ $\quad$ $\dfrac{12}{4} =$ $\quad$ $\dfrac{35}{5} =$ $\quad$ $\dfrac{2}{1} =$ $\quad$ $\dfrac{4}{4} =$ $\quad$ $\dfrac{32}{8} =$ $\quad$ $\dfrac{16}{8} =$ $\quad$ $\dfrac{7}{1} =$ $\quad$ $\dfrac{14}{7} =$

$\dfrac{45}{9} =$ $\quad$ $\dfrac{8}{1} =$ $\quad$ $\dfrac{6}{6} =$ $\quad$ $\dfrac{0}{9} =$ $\quad$ $\dfrac{21}{7} =$ $\quad$ $\dfrac{30}{6} =$ $\quad$ $\dfrac{0}{3} =$ $\quad$ $\dfrac{6}{2} =$ $\quad$ $\dfrac{0}{5} =$ $\quad$ $\dfrac{35}{5} =$

$\dfrac{20}{5} =$ $\quad$ $\dfrac{6}{3} =$ $\quad$ $\dfrac{42}{7} =$ $\quad$ $\dfrac{18}{3} =$ $\quad$ $\dfrac{5}{1} =$ $\quad$ $\dfrac{28}{4} =$ $\quad$ $\dfrac{12}{4} =$ $\quad$ $\dfrac{28}{7} =$ $\quad$ $\dfrac{15}{3} =$ $\quad$ $\dfrac{6}{3} =$

$\dfrac{24}{6} =$ $\quad$ $\dfrac{72}{9} =$ $\quad$ $\dfrac{4}{1} =$ $\quad$ $\dfrac{16}{2} =$ $\quad$ $\dfrac{36}{6} =$ $\quad$ $\dfrac{15}{3} =$ $\quad$ $\dfrac{48}{6} =$ $\quad$ $\dfrac{1}{1} =$ $\quad$ $\dfrac{7}{7} =$ $\quad$ $\dfrac{81}{9} =$

$\dfrac{16}{4} =$ $\quad$ $\dfrac{2}{2} =$ $\quad$ $\dfrac{40}{5} =$ $\quad$ $\dfrac{35}{7} =$ $\quad$ $\dfrac{8}{8} =$ $\quad$ $\dfrac{14}{7} =$ $\quad$ $\dfrac{30}{5} =$ $\quad$ $\dfrac{0}{6} =$ $\quad$ $\dfrac{27}{9} =$ $\quad$ $\dfrac{54}{6} =$

$\dfrac{7}{7} =$ $\quad$ $\dfrac{45}{5} =$ $\quad$ $\dfrac{18}{9} =$ $\quad$ $\dfrac{8}{4} =$ $\quad$ $\dfrac{14}{2} =$ $\quad$ $\dfrac{8}{2} =$ $\quad$ $\dfrac{10}{2} =$ $\quad$ $\dfrac{64}{8} =$ $\quad$ $\dfrac{4}{2} =$ $\quad$ $\dfrac{4}{4} =$

$\dfrac{12}{2} =$ $\quad$ $\dfrac{12}{6} =$ $\quad$ $\dfrac{0}{2} =$ $\quad$ $\dfrac{42}{6} =$ $\quad$ $\dfrac{20}{4} =$ $\quad$ $\dfrac{36}{9} =$ $\quad$ $\dfrac{56}{7} =$ $\quad$ $\dfrac{12}{3} =$ $\quad$ $\dfrac{32}{4} =$ $\quad$ $\dfrac{12}{2} =$

Name .
(Draw a $4\frac{1}{4}$" line segment.)

Date .

(Draw a line segment 2" shorter than the name line. _____ ")

1. Kyle reads 10 pages each weekday and 20 pages on each day of the weekend. How many pages will he read in one week?

   Number sentence _____ Answer _____

   How many pages will he read in 4 weeks?

   Number sentence _____ Answer _____

2. Each rectangle is a candy bar. Write the correct fraction inside each piece.

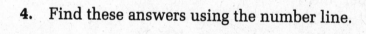

   Which fraction is greater? _____

3. Show two minutes of nine on the clocks.

4. Find these answers using the number line.

   $-3 + 2 =$ _____

   $3 + -2 =$ _____

   (number line: −7 −6 −5 −4 −3 −2 −1 0 1 2 3 4 5 6 7)

   (number line: −7 −6 −5 −4 −3 −2 −1 0 1 2 3 4 5 6 7)

5. Find the answers.

   $450 - 87 =$ _____

   $\frac{2}{7} + \frac{4}{7} =$ _____

   $\begin{array}{r} 5,2\,8\,0 \\ \times\qquad 5 \\ \hline \end{array}$

   $\begin{array}{r} \$8\,3,9\,1\,2.3\,7 \\ +\ \ 7,9\,2\,8.7\,5 \\ \hline \end{array}$

   $8\overline{)84}$

   $3\overline{)824}$

   $5\overline{)457}$

3-137Wa

Name _____   **LESSON 137B**
                                                  Math 3
Date _____

1. Shannon draws 3 pictures each weekday and 5 pictures on each day of the weekend.
   How many pictures will she draw in one week?

   Number sentence _____ Answer _____

   How many pictures will she draw in 6 weeks?

   Number sentence _____ Answer _____

2. Each rectangle is a candy bar. Write the correct fraction inside each piece.

   Which fraction is greater? _____

3. Show fifteen minutes of four on the clocks.

   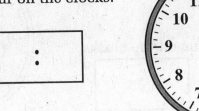   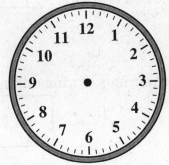

4. Find these answers using the number line.

   $-2 + -3 =$ _____ $-5 + 1 =$ _____

5. Find the answers. (Remember: Simplify the multiplication and division first.)

   $9 + 6 \times 3 - 9 \div 3 + 6 =$ _____   6,1 2 0 $5 6,2 1 9.3 0
                                               $\times$ 6   +   8,9 5 3.7 5

   $320 - 53 =$ _____ $\dfrac{5}{8} + \dfrac{2}{8} =$ _____

            $6\overline{)65}$ $2\overline{)730}$ $4\overline{)325}$

Name _____ Score: _____ **D1-100**

6 ÷ 3 =	20 ÷ 5 =	9 ÷ 9 =	12 ÷ 4 =	10 ÷ 2 =
40 ÷ 8 =	1 ÷ 1 =	36 ÷ 6 =	63 ÷ 7 =	16 ÷ 4 =
35 ÷ 5 =	6 ÷ 1 =	18 ÷ 3 =	21 ÷ 7 =	81 ÷ 9 =
6 ÷ 2 =	16 ÷ 8 =	20 ÷ 4 =	7 ÷ 1 =	54 ÷ 6 =
6 ÷ 6 =	40 ÷ 5 =	9 ÷ 1 =	0 ÷ 8 =	27 ÷ 3 =
64 ÷ 8 =	14 ÷ 7 =	8 ÷ 2 =	0 ÷ 4 =	27 ÷ 9 =
24 ÷ 8 =	15 ÷ 3 =	16 ÷ 2 =	45 ÷ 9 =	18 ÷ 6 =
2 ÷ 1 =	25 ÷ 5 =	12 ÷ 3 =	16 ÷ 4 =	56 ÷ 7 =
25 ÷ 5 =	16 ÷ 2 =	7 ÷ 7 =	32 ÷ 4 =	72 ÷ 8 =
4 ÷ 2 =	30 ÷ 6 =	12 ÷ 3 =	18 ÷ 9 =	6 ÷ 6 =
5 ÷ 1 =	8 ÷ 8 =	36 ÷ 4 =	0 ÷ 2 =	54 ÷ 9 =
35 ÷ 7 =	9 ÷ 3 =	5 ÷ 5 =	12 ÷ 6 =	24 ÷ 3 =
24 ÷ 6 =	7 ÷ 1 =	30 ÷ 5 =	21 ÷ 3 =	6 ÷ 6 =
14 ÷ 2 =	72 ÷ 9 =	8 ÷ 4 =	0 ÷ 7 =	48 ÷ 8 =
63 ÷ 9 =	3 ÷ 3 =	28 ÷ 7 =	3 ÷ 1 =	42 ÷ 6 =
4 ÷ 4 =	32 ÷ 8 =	2 ÷ 2 =	36 ÷ 9 =	0 ÷ 5 =
12 ÷ 2 =	42 ÷ 7 =	10 ÷ 5 =	24 ÷ 4 =	8 ÷ 1 =
49 ÷ 7 =	9 ÷ 3 =	0 ÷ 9 =	12 ÷ 6 =	56 ÷ 8 =
28 ÷ 4 =	24 ÷ 8 =	0 ÷ 3 =	48 ÷ 6 =	10 ÷ 2 =
18 ÷ 9 =	4 ÷ 1 =	25 ÷ 5 =	48 ÷ 8 =	21 ÷ 7 =

3-138Fa

Name _____

(Measure this line segment. _____")

Date •

(Draw a line segment 1" shorter than the name line. _____")

1. Laura won a jar of 720 hard candies in the guessing contest at the fair. She will share the candy with Joan and Sue. How many candies will each girl receive?

Number sentence _____

Answer _____

2. Use the number line to find these answers.

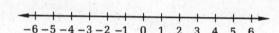

$2 + 4 =$ _____ $-2 + 4 =$ _____

$2 + -4 =$ _____ $-2 + -4 =$ _____

3. The time shown on the clock is _____ minutes of _____.

Write the digital time.

4. Find the answers.

$(3 + 7) \times 4 + 3^2$ $9 + 2 \times 3 - 6 \div 3 + 3$

5. Which lines are parallel? _____ and _____

Which lines are perpendicular? _____ and _____

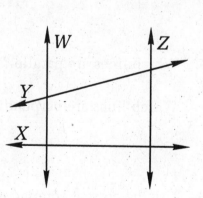

6. Use the correct comparison symbol (<, >, or =).

$\frac{56}{7} + \sqrt{81}$ ☐ $\frac{40}{5} + \sqrt{64}$ $32 \div 4 + 800 \div 10$ ☐ $28 + 64$

Name _____

Date _____

1. Wayne and his three brothers have 632 baseball cards. If they divide the cards equally, how many cards will each boy have?

   Number sentence _____

   Answer _____

2. Use the number line to find these answers.

   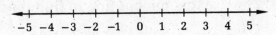

   $3 + 1 =$ _____ $-3 + 1 =$ _____

   $3 + -1 =$ _____ $-3 + -1 =$ _____

3. The time shown on the clock is _____ minutes of _____.

   Write the digital time.

   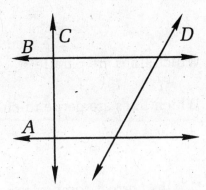

4. Find the answers.

   $(7 + 2) \times 3 + 4^2$ $4 \times 5 - 2 \times 3 + 6 \div 2$

5. Which lines are parallel? _____ and _____

   Which lines are perpendicular? _____ and _____

6. Use the correct comparison symbol (<, >, or =).

   $\frac{56}{7} + \sqrt{64}$ ☐ $\frac{35}{5} + 3^2$ $32 \div 8 + 60 \div 10$ ☐ $81 - 72$

Name _____

Today's Date is _____

Today's Pattern
_____
_____

Coin Cup

Q	D	N	P	Total Coins

Today's Problem
_____

Today's Date is _____

Today's Pattern
_____
_____

Coin Cup

Q	D	N	P	Total Coins

Today's Problem
_____

Today's Date is _____

Today's Pattern
_____
_____

Coin Cup

Q	D	N	P	Total Coins

Today's Problem
_____

Today's Date is _____

Today's Pattern
_____
_____

Coin Cup

Q	D	N	P	Total Coins

Today's Problem
_____

Today's Date is _____

Today's Pattern
_____
_____

Coin Cup

Q	D	N	P	Total Coins

Today's Problem
_____

$5\overline{)15}$	$2\overline{)8}$	$7\overline{)49}$	$1\overline{)3}$	$6\overline{)6}$	$9\overline{)27}$	$5\overline{)30}$	$4\overline{)12}$	$8\overline{)32}$	$3\overline{)21}$
$2\overline{)2}$	$5\overline{)40}$	$9\overline{)72}$	$3\overline{)3}$	$7\overline{)28}$	$4\overline{)4}$	$8\overline{)16}$	$3\overline{)6}$	$6\overline{)42}$	$1\overline{)1}$
$4\overline{)24}$	$7\overline{)0}$	$3\overline{)15}$	$8\overline{)48}$	$2\overline{)4}$	$6\overline{)24}$	$1\overline{)7}$	$9\overline{)18}$	$5\overline{)25}$	$2\overline{)0}$
$6\overline{)18}$	$9\overline{)45}$	$2\overline{)12}$	$5\overline{)5}$	$3\overline{)18}$	$7\overline{)56}$	$1\overline{)0}$	$4\overline{)36}$	$6\overline{)12}$	$8\overline{)40}$
$7\overline{)14}$	$1\overline{)2}$	$5\overline{)45}$	$2\overline{)10}$	$8\overline{)24}$	$4\overline{)0}$	$6\overline{)30}$	$3\overline{)12}$	$1\overline{)9}$	$9\overline{)36}$
$9\overline{)9}$	$4\overline{)20}$	$6\overline{)48}$	$3\overline{)9}$	$5\overline{)0}$	$2\overline{)6}$	$8\overline{)64}$	$4\overline{)8}$	$1\overline{)6}$	$7\overline{)63}$
$3\overline{)24}$	$8\overline{)56}$	$2\overline{)18}$	$4\overline{)16}$	$9\overline{)54}$	$5\overline{)20}$	$1\overline{)5}$	$7\overline{)21}$	$8\overline{)72}$	$6\overline{)0}$
$5\overline{)10}$	$1\overline{)3}$	$9\overline{)63}$	$8\overline{)8}$	$3\overline{)27}$	$7\overline{)42}$	$2\overline{)16}$	$9\overline{)0}$	$6\overline{)18}$	$4\overline{)28}$
$1\overline{)4}$	$9\overline{)27}$	$7\overline{)35}$	$2\overline{)14}$	$6\overline{)36}$	$3\overline{)9}$	$8\overline{)0}$	$4\overline{)32}$	$5\overline{)30}$	$7\overline{)7}$
$8\overline{)40}$	$6\overline{)36}$	$3\overline{)0}$	$9\overline{)72}$	$1\overline{)8}$	$5\overline{)15}$	$7\overline{)21}$	$2\overline{)16}$	$3\overline{)15}$	$4\overline{)24}$

Name
(Draw a 9 cm 4 mm line segment.)

Date •

(Draw a line segment 2 cm shorter than the name line. _____ cm _____ mm)

1. Carl weighed 8 pounds, 5 ounces when he was born. What was his weight in ounces? (1 pound = 16 ounces)

   Number sentence _____

   Answer _____

2. Graph these points on the coordinate plane.

   A: (−3, 2)
   B: (4, 2)
   C: (4, −1)
   D: (−3, −1)

   Connect the points in alphabetical order. (Connect D to A.)

   What shape did you make? _____

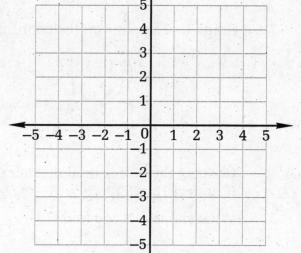

3. Write these fractions in order from least to greatest.

   $\dfrac{1}{16}$, $\dfrac{1}{3}$, $\dfrac{1}{2}$, $\dfrac{1}{8}$, $\dfrac{1}{4}$

   _____ , _____ , _____ , _____ , _____

4. Find the answers.

   −1 + 3 = _____   −3 + 1 = _____

   −1 + −3 = _____   3 + 1 = _____

   (number line from −5 to 5)

5. How many days are there in the first 6 months of the year? _____

6. Find the answers.

   $30 - (3 + 2) + 4^2 =$ _____ $\dfrac{9}{10} - \dfrac{7}{10} =$ _____

   $4\overline{)903}$ $6 \times 7 + 3 \times 2 - 14 \div 7 =$ _____

Name _____   **LESSON 139B**
                                                      Math 3
Date _____

1. Chelsea weighed 7 pounds, 10 ounces when she was born. What was her weight in ounces? (1 pound = 16 ounces)

   Number sentence _____

   Answer _____

2. Graph these points on the coordinate plane.

        E: $(-4, 1)$
        F: $(1, 1)$
        G: $(1, -4)$
        H: $(-4, -4)$

   Connect the points in alphabetical order.
   (Connect H to E.)

   What shape did you make? _____

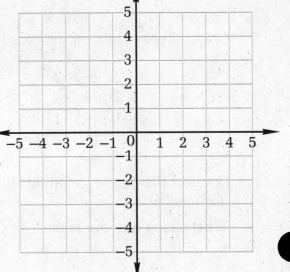

3. Write these fractions in order from least to greatest.

   $\frac{1}{6}, \frac{1}{3}, \frac{1}{2}, \frac{1}{8}, \frac{1}{4}$ _____ , _____ , _____ , _____ , _____

4. Find the answers.

   $2 + 5 =$ _____ $5 + -2 =$ _____

   $-2 + -5 =$ _____ $5 + 2 =$ _____

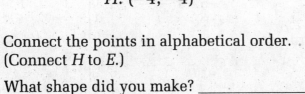

5. How many days are there in the last 6 months of the year? _____

6. Find the answers.

   $2 \times (3 + 4) + 6^2 =$ _____ $\frac{5}{6} - \frac{2}{6} =$ _____

   $5\overline{)629}$ $5 \times 3 - 49 \div 7 + 30 \div 5 =$ _____

1. Santo is ten years old. He is seven years younger than his sister. How old is his sister?

difference

larger   smaller

_____ _____

Number sentence _____

Answer _____

2. Mrs. Hyde bought a package of 96 markers. She divided them equally among 6 children. How many markers did she give each child?

Number sentence _____

Answer _____

3. Each rectangle is a candy bar. Write the correct fraction inside each piece.

Which fraction shows the smallest piece? _____

Which fraction shows the largest piece? _____

4. Show ten minutes of two on the clocks.

5. Find the answers.

$5\overline{)74}$ $3\overline{)87}$ $2\overline{)346}$

6. Use the graph to answer the questions.

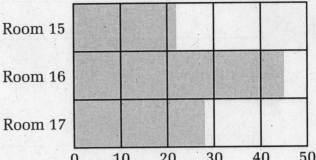

About how many books did the children in each room read?

Room 15 _____

Room 16 _____

Room 17 _____

About how many books did they read altogether? _____

About how many more books did the children in Room 16 read than the children in Room 17?

Answer _____

7. Find these answers.

$2 + 5 =$ _____ $-2 + 5 =$ _____

$-2 + -5 =$ _____ $2 + -5 =$ _____

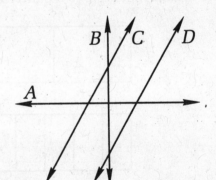

8. Which lines are parallel? _____ and _____

Which lines are perpendicular? _____ and _____

9. Use the correct comparison symbol (>, <, or =).

3^2 ☐ $600 \div 100$ $4 + 6 \times 3$ ☐ 5^2 $\sqrt{81} + \sqrt{100}$ ☐ $72 - 53$

$\dfrac{24}{6}$ ☐ $21 \div 3$ 6×200 ☐ $(100 - 88) \times 100$

10. Find the answers.

$624 + 259 + 33 =$ _____ $900 - 127 =$ _____ $4 \times 1{,}857 =$ _____

Name _____

Graph these ordered pairs.

Connect the points in alphabetical order.

A: (4, 2)	*B*: (6, 1)	*C*: (7, 0)
D: (7, –1)	*E*: (6, –3)	*F*: (2, –4)
G: (–1, –3)	*H*: (–3, –2)	*I*: (–5, –4)
J: (–5, 2)	*K*: (–3, 0)	*L*: (0, 1)
M: (3, 2)		

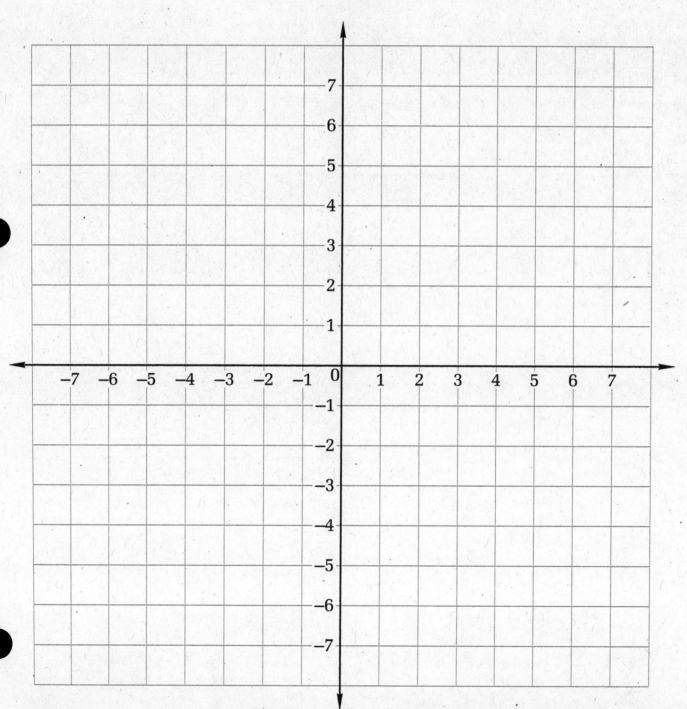

3-140 Ma